THE NUMINOUS LEGACY

The Numinous Legacy

Modern Cosmology

and Religion

Adair Butchins

ALBATROSS PRESS

© Adair Butchins 2002

First published in 2002 by Albatross Press Ltd
MM House
3-7 Wyndham Street
Aldershot, Hants, GU12 4NY

Distributed by Gazelle Book Services Limited, Falcon House Queen
Square Lancaster, England LA1 1RN

British Library Cataloguing in Publication Data
A catalogue record for this book is available from the British Library

ISBN 0-9539818-0-0

Typeset by Amolibros, Watchet, Somerset
This book production has been managed by Amolibros
Printed and bound by T J International, Padstow, Cornwall, UK

Contents

Diagrams, Tables & Illustrations   ix

Preface   xi

Prologue   xiii

Introduction   1
Where is God in the universe if anywhere?

The abode of God – the limitations of scientists – the Copernican Principle appears to invalidate Western religions – some religious and atheistic reactions to the Copernican Principle – special and general relativity – confirmation of the Copernican Principle – a digression on certain mathematical concepts

Chapter One The Copernican Principle   15
Why should we be so special?

The pre- and post-Copernican eras in cosmology and religion – the formation of religious and cosmological concepts – monotheism and the Greek enlightenment – the moving earth – Plato's theory of forms – realists and nominalists – the Islamic contention – Christian Judaic cosmology – the challenge to the Church – the secular implication – the Eastern impact – summary

Chapter Two Space 43
Where does it all come from?

Distance measurements – the probability of extra-terrestrial civilisations – island universes – the Redshift – the displacement of humankind and religious apologia – life in the universe – a possible *real* UFO – an historical analogy – further apologetics – free will – summary

Chapter Three Time 66
Where does it all go to?

The age of the universe – the cosmic microwave background – the death of the steady state theory and Olber's paradox – the problem of hidden matter and the Apocalypse – thermodynamics and the Heat Death – the fate of planet earth and the Book of Revelation – the evolution of man – summary

Chapter Four Contingency 82
Could the universe have been different?

Dawkin's argument contested – Payley's argument extended – a brief history of the universe and the measurement of time – special conditions for the formation of life – Penrose, Hawking and others – summary

Chapter Five Boundaries 96
What goes in between universes?

The many worlds theory – the structure of boundaries – inflation – the steady state resurrected – inflation contested – the COBE discovery – summary

Chapter Six The Anthropic Principle   109
Was the universe made for us?

Gerald Schroeder, God's spin-doctor – the application
of the Anthropic Principle – the evolution of universes –
were we constructed by a super-civilisation? – a prima-
donna God – computer immortality and the Omega Point
– resurrection of the dead by emulation – are we perfectly
adaptable? – the theological argument – the faith of
religion and the faith of science – summary

Chapter Seven The Problem of Evil   138
Why did God make germs?

The Pandora problem – the happy sin – the Tale of the
Good Brahmin – Deism and Theism – the Kabbalah –
dualism – summary

Chapter Eight Consciousness   150
What makes brains think?

A cosmological basis for consciousness – elementary brain
structure – Table One – consciousness unexplained – the
theorem of Godel – the parallel universe – tests for a
parallel universe – the normal distribution – neurological
evidence – near death – summary

Chapter Nine Conclusions   183
What is reality?

Hinduism – Sikhs – Jainism – Parsis – Buddhism –
Confucianism – Taoism – religions of Japan – mysticism
and science – the Western religions – Judaism –
Christianity – Islam – religion and the parallel universe
– ethics as an emergent property – ethical reductionism
questioned – the necessity of ethical foundations –
epilogue

Appendix   212
Responses by religious authorities

Glossary   242

Bibliography   248

Index   258

Diagrams, Tables and Illustrations

	Page
Copernicus	xx
Alighieri Dante	4
Albert Einstein	11
Diagram One: The method of Aristarchus	23
Plato and Aristotle	25
Thomas Paine	38
Diagram Two: Distance measurement of Mars by parallax 1671	44
Diagram Three: Horizontal parallax	46
Table One: The Christian/Judiac timescale of creation	68
Table Two: The scientific timeascale of the universe	69
Charles Darwin	84
Table Three: Brain functions	154
Diagram Four: The human brain	155
René Descartes	157
Diagram Five: Electrical and chemical brain reactions	163
Diagram Six: Normal distribution of intelligent life; normal distribution of genetic mutations.	168

Colour Plate Section, facing page 108

Separate Universes

Bubble Universes

Russian Doll Universes

Intersecting Universes

Preface

'Into this Universe, and *Why* not knowing,
Nor *Whence*, like Water willy-nilly flowing:
And out of it, as Wind along the Waste,
I know not *Whither*, willy-nilly blowing.'

Rubaiyat of Omar Khayyam. Quatrain 32
Translated by Edward Fitzgerald

Before becoming an academic, I spent many years travelling the world in various occupations. I found that most people are fascinated by the night sky and the concept of the endless universe. In particular they inevitably link this concept with religion. Why is there something instead of nothing? Where and how does humankind relate to the universal order of things? If the answers given by religious authorities seem unsatisfactory, can they be replaced by scientific reasoning? Is some vital factor still missing from our philosophy?

This book is aimed at the intelligent reader, curious about our place in the universe. In general, the readers of such topics are interested not only in the science presented but in a further question. Where does this leave religion? Most scientists tend to shy away from religion as a very contentious subject, which of course it is. On the other hand, there are those firm believers, scientists or otherwise, who write religious apologies in the scientific idiom; for instance, Schroeder's *Genesis and the Big Bang* and Peacock's *A Brief History of Eternity*.

To quote from Rabbi Rayner's letter in the appendix to the present work:

'I am very glad that you are writing a book on the effect of cosmology on religion and shall be immensely interested in what your research uncovers. My impression is that it has been considered only (a) by fundamentalists, in a vain attempt to refute it, and (b) by the more radical and philosophically minded theologians.'

The Numinous Legacy attempts to tackle the subject of scientific cosmology and its bearing on received religion from an impartial point of view. The latest cosmological ideas and theories are explained in as straightforward a manner as possible together with any associated religious implications. This entails a certain amount of concentration on the part of the reader but nothing like the amount required for many of the books on cosmology by specialist authors.

I consider that this book is important for the general reader because, although refuting religious fundamentalism, it does not refute religious belief as such. Although there seems to be a general impression that science has completely demolished religion, this book shows that there are still perfectly valid arguments for, as well as against, the existence of a Creator. It also shows that there are aspects of the universe that still defy scientific explanation and that a correspondence between mysticism and modern physics, whereby the observer is an essential factor, has a resonance with cosmology.

I am afraid that it will not necessarily please all the priests, the rabbis and the mullahs, but you can't please everybody and it contains nothing remotely blasphemous.

The book is based not only on my own research but also, largely, on the lectures I have given and the discussions I have had with my fellow academics, both scientific and religious.

When asked about my own beliefs I usually reply that on Fridays, Saturdays and Sundays I believe in God but for the rest of the week I am an agnostic or sometimes even an atheist.

Adair Butchins

Prologue

Some years ago, I listened to a television interview with the famous Jewish physicist Richard Feynman. He was being asked why he no longer adhered to the Jewish religion or believed in God. His reply was interesting. I cannot remember the exact words, but it went something like this:

> 'It's too local, have you looked at the sky? Do you know what's out there?'

As a student of cosmology, I immediately understood his reference to the scale and immensity of the universe. It seemed inconceivable to him that all these religious myths and stories referring to our insignificant planet as the centre and epitome of creation, could have any real relevance to the universe that modern cosmology presents to us. I felt an immediate sympathy for his instinctive feeling that 'there was something, if not rotten, then at least illusory in the state of Denmark', as far as religion was concerned.

Many religious apologists now reiterate that the greater the universe, the greater and more marvellous the act of God's creation. That misses the point, however, that God's creation was supposed to have centred on us. Once we divest ourselves of this belief, we find ourselves in unknown territory. What now is the purpose of the universe, if there is a purpose? How can this entire religious apologia reconcile us to the universal heat-death? How many other civilisations exist or have existed on other planets in other galaxies? What of their religious convictions?

Unfortunately, we are never likely to find out. It is possible but extremely improbable that any such contemporary civilisation will be near enough, even for speed of light communication to take place. There is a great deal of science-fiction writing addressing this subject, in addition to films and television series. Films like *Independence Day* or *Star Wars*, with stunning special effects including loud sounds and bangs that mysteriously take place in the almost complete vacuum of outer space. Television series such as *Star Trek* or *Dr Who*, in which, every week a new populated planet is discovered, where the inhabitants, however weird, all speak English. Then there are the UFO spotters and in some cases UFO kidnappers. These stories now seem to have taken the place of those, fashionable in the Middle Ages, of meeting Satan or seeing witches fly through the air on broomsticks. Certain religious apologists, David Wilkinson for example, (see Chapter Two) use this media-based fiction in an attempt to discredit contemporary scientific reasoning. They claim this nonsense to be the province of science and then happily go about discrediting it. In fact, they are attacking a straw man. No genuine scientist would claim that highly developed alien civilisations are within easy reach of our planet. What is claimed is much more modest and believable – that although it is possible for other civilisations to arise within our galaxy, the probability of their present existence is remote, even in a galaxy of two hundred billion stars. Nevertheless, we can observe billions of distant galaxies, and undoubtedly, countless billions more are unobserved. There is no scientific reason to discount the existence of other alien civilisations within this vast panorama, although they are outside the limits of any possible contact.

What is it that these religious apologists are afraid of? It appears that they fear for the very basis of their religion. It is interesting that other religious apologists who are prepared to take modern cosmology within their scope do not, in general, ascribe to the more orthodox version of their religions. For example, Murphy and Ellis (see Chapter Nine) adopt the view of the Quaker and Anabaptist version of Christianity, which does not insist upon the exclusivity of the mainstream version. The Sufi sect of Islam regards the idea of God as transcendent and would encompass the whole universe, finite or infinite, including all life forms within His realm. The religions of the orient do not seem to have the same problems with respect to the universality of life as the three great monotheistic religions of the west, Judaism, Christianity, and to a lesser extent, Islam. In some respect and for the same reasons, the fundamentalist beliefs of these religions suffer under the same delusion as astrology.

Before the advent of modern cosmology, astrology held a convincing place in the study of the stars. It maintained a hold over both the general population and the ruling classes, and to a certain extent is still widely believed today.

From a historical point of view, how the ancients regarded the effectiveness and validity of astrological readings and predictions is a fascinating subject. It tells us a great deal about the psychology of the ancient sages.

From a scientific point of view, however, the subject of astrology is considered fallacious. The whole concept of the zodiacal signs was dreamt up by the highly imaginative Babylonians and inherited by the ancient Greeks and Romans. Who could possibly find a bear in Ursa Major or a bull in Taurus unless first told that that is what they were supposed to be? The Greeks and Romans adapted the signs to their own mythology and sought to find an affiliation between them and human affairs. As a matter of interest, the Chinese did the same thing but unsurprisingly constructed entirely different constellations.

The Greeks, with the notable exception of Aristarchus (see Chapter One), considered the universe geocentric and the earth populated by men and gods. The stars were supposed to be attached to a crystal sphere, revolving daily on an axis through the earth. Each of the five known planets and the sun and moon were attached to revolving spheres of their own. The distances of these spheres from the earth were fixed in accordance with certain speculative notions as to numbers and music. Hence, gifted persons might at times be privileged to hear 'the music of the spheres'. The belief in this basic heavenly structure continued throughout the Middle Ages. Even Copernicus after propounding the heliocentric system believed in the crystal stellar sphere.

The Greeks and Romans envisaged a correspondence between the earth and the stellar sphere, since the gods set many of the characters of Greek mythology among the stars, for example, Castor and Pollux the heavenly twins or Cygnus the swan. This gave rise to a belief that the star constellations could affect the affairs of man on earth, both individually and en mass.

For many, this belief has persisted unto the present day, even though the basis for it has been demolished by modern astronomy. Today we realise that the constellation patterns in the sky are really an illusion. Looked at in three dimensions they disappear. For example, in Ursa Major the star Alkaid is further away from Mizar than we are. The stars also have proper motions of their own in the galaxy and even the two-dimensional patterns will be changing over time. In addition, the constellations of the Zodiac have a retrograde motion along the ecliptic due to the precession of the equinoxes. They do a complete cycle in 26,000 years. The astrologers seem not to have noticed, since the birth zodiacal signs are still designated as they were at the time of Hipparchus in the second century BC. In fact, if your birth sign is given as Aries, say, it is really Pisces.

Modern physics can give no method by which the stars and planets can influence events or individuals on earth. There are four known forces of physics. The strong and weak forces that have very small ranges within the size of the atom and are thus not relevant; together with the electric and gravitational forces. The electric force from the stars and planets reaches us in the form of electro-magnetic radiation, i.e. starlight, radio waves, cosmic rays, etc. These are incredibly weak when compared to the emissions from the sun as we can see when we compare starlight to sunlight. The main effect of the gravitational force from the heavens comes from the sun and moon, which together cause the tides. The gravitational force of the planet Venus for instance, upon a new-born baby, is about one hundred million times less than that of the earth. That exerted by the stars would be far weaker.

Astrology still has as its basis the ancient heavenly structure of crystal spheres, described above. It makes it an absorbing study with regard to religion. In the ancient world, Islam accepted astronomy as a science, but the religious leaders strongly condemned astrology, since the *Koran* states that 'nobody but Allah can know the future'. Christianity took a similar view. Astrology was fiercely condemned both by St Augustine and St Thomas Aquinas. It was considered not only wicked but also false. They considered that this could be proved by the different fortunes of twins who have the same horoscope. The Stoic conception of astrological fate was considered mistaken since angels and men have free will. Astrology in fact is originally a pagan practice, which, in spite of condemnation, was taken up by various sages and scholars in all three of the great monotheistic Western Religions. It is necessary to distinguish between its impact upon history, which is important, and its scientific validity, which is non-existent.

The same, in many respects, can be said of the fundamental beliefs of the monotheistic religions, although as we shall see in the following pages, the belief in a Deity is still relevant as one valid interpretation of the universe.

This book represents a personal investigation into the effects of modern cosmology upon religion. The ideas and presentations have come from many and diverse sources both literary and verbal. I must thank Professor George Ellis of the University of Cape Town who first introduced me to modern cosmology and whose subsequent work I have found invaluable in the formation of my ideas and arguments. I must also thank Rabbis David Goldberg and John Rayner of the Liberal Synagogue, St John's Wood, London, as well as Rabbi Simon Felix of the Chief Rabbi's Office. For editorial assistance and structural advice, my thanks go to Robert Lambolle. The Roman Catholic contribution included Newman House and Dr P E Hodgson of Corpus Christie College. I am grateful to the Rev Dr John Polkinghorne and the Rev Dr

Russell Stannard as well as the Rt Rev and Rt Hon Richard Chartres, Bishop of London, for the Protestant contribution. I have had useful and informative discussions with Usama Hasan and Shoaib Qureshi of the Muslim Research Society. Natalie d'Arbelof has made many useful comments. My son Richard and my daughter Jane have added their ideas for improvements. I thank Tony Denton and Richard Unthank for their design work. I am obliged to the National Portrait Gallery and Hulton Getty Picture Library for illustrations. Jane Tatam has supervised the publishing and finally my wife Janet helped enormously by proof-reading and supplying me with endless cups of tea and a great deal of forbearance.

Adair Butchins

Copernicus

Introduction

Where is God in the universe?
If anywhere!

In a small village near Naples called Nola, on 1st May 1548 was born a child of remarkable talent. He was christened Felipe Giordano. His father, Gioan Bruno, was a soldier and a friend of the poet Tansillo.

Felipe had a happy childhood. As an exceptionally intelligent boy, he would ask many searching questions, particularly concerning the validity of accepted truth and wisdom. This habit remained with him all his life and was eventually to be the cause of his death at the stake on 17th February 1600.

When very young he claimed to have seen spirits on the hills. We do not know whether this was optical illusion or just poetic fancy, but at any rate he quickly became much more sceptical in his outlook and came to the conclusion, unusual for the sixteenth century, that nothing was to be believed without thorough investigation and verification. It seems that he came to this conclusion in the following manner. As a child playing on the fertile slopes of Mount Cicada, he often looked across at the apparently barren face of Vesuvius. One day he crossed the valley and to his astonishment found similar luxurious vines and orchards on Vesuvius; while looking back at Mount Cicada he discerned the same barren appearance that he had previously associated with Vesuvius.

Thus, he discovered not only that things are not always what they seem but that on the large scale things can have the same appearance even when viewed from different positions. In time, Giordano Bruno, impressed by the writings of Nicholas de Cusa (see Chapter One) and the heliocentric theory of Copernicus, extended this idea to the universe as a whole. Thus in its basic form was propounded what would become the Copernican Principle of the homogeneity of the universe. In other words, the universe on the large scale would present the same appearance and have the same structure, irrespective of the observer's position.

Giordano considered the universe to consist of an infinite number of worlds, which he identified as the stars contained in infinite space. This idea caused problems for the church. Even Copernicus had conceived of the earth as a planet occupying one of a series of rotating spheres and the stars as motionless and fixed in their positions on the eighth sphere. The Copernican universe was a finite and rigidly bounded whole with God firmly established in His heaven. However, by dispelling the earth from the centre of the universe, Copernicus had let loose a plethora of cosmological heresies. If the universe was infinite and the spheres were non-existent, where was God in the universe? If anywhere.

This was not, in general, a question that would be asked before the advent of Copernicus because everybody knew where God was. He was in heaven with His angels and perhaps the souls of the blest. Previously, in pagan times, He had dwelt on the tops of mountains or in the sun. This is because the universe at that time was constructed around Planet earth, our own physical world, which was vast.

It is difficult to imagine in these days of high-speed transport and instant communication how enormous the world seemed to the ancients. The fastest transport available was a sailing ship and then only with a favourable wind. Journeys that we now traverse in hours would take months, often with considerable hardship. It was perfectly natural to consider our planet to be the whole universe with its extended horizons and undiscovered realms, with mountains leading to heaven and caves leading to hell.

The Abode of God

Alighieri Dante explained the basic concept of the abode of God in detail in his famous poem *The Divine Comedy.*

The poem opens in the year 1300 on the morning of Good Friday. The poet is lost in a dark and fearful forest. He attempts to escape by climbing a mountain bathed in light but three wild beasts; symbols of the world's temptations confront him. The poet Virgil's shade appears, saying that the Blessed Virgin and Dante's Beatrice have sent him, to lead the poet through the regions of the next world. Together they travel through hell, meeting many famous people both ancient and contemporary. Each is undergoing punishment according to their sins. At the innermost depth of the abyss is the monstrous Lucifer, held fast in ice.

They climb down his body and finally reach the surface of the earth again by a rocky path through the earth's centre. Then they climb Mount Purgatory and encounter the souls hoping for Paradise after atonement. Onward they continue climbing towards Paradise, but a wall of flame bars their path. Dante, seeing Beatrice beyond, leaps through. Beatrice now leads the poet through Paradise. At last, Dante, although not allowed into the Supreme Heaven, is vouchsafed a brief understanding of the glory of God.

Thus was understood the geography of the universe, complete with heaven and hell. What becomes of this geography when the earth is but one planet of many orbiting the sun? How can this possibly accord with Dante's vision if the universe is infinite throughout space? Is God anywhere or nowhere?

Thus, both cosmology and religion were ongoing processes inextricably intertwined. Modern cosmology is a result of the scientific revolution brought about by the Renaissance. It paints a picture of the universe that is far more exotic and amazing than anything the ancient religious myths and traditions would have us believe. Modern Western theology attempts to incorporate this cosmology by replacing, or at least reconciling, the God of Abraham, Isaac and Jacob with the God of the galaxies, the quasars and the Big Bang.

Alighieri Dante

We will also view such cosmology from the vantage of Eastern theology, both theistic and atheistic; and in addition, consider both consciousness and the position of ethics in the modern cosmos.

This is particularly relevant with regard to the recent introduction of the modern political 'religions' of Nazism with its pagan and Nietzschean overtones and Communism with its apocalyptic belief in the final socialist utopia.

The Limitations of Scientists

In astronomy and cosmology, it is true that those experts, who have a firm grasp of the relevant mathematical physics, have an insight into such matters denied to the non-professional. This results in a common outlook of awe and amazement among many people with regard to scientists and mathematicians. The esoteric subjects of 'black holes' and 'other universes' have a ring of magic about them. It is almost like the ancient attitude towards alchemists. The fact that nowadays such scholars are respectable scientists and mathematicians, rather than charlatans, lends credibility to their views and ideas, not only with respect to their own subjects but also to other allied subjects, especially philosophy and religion.

Having studied the subject of cosmology myself, I have concluded that such credibility is often misplaced. Take the philosophical concept of consciousness, for example. We shall see in Chapter Six that even the most distinguished scientist can no more explain the phenomenon of consciousness than the greengrocer in the corner shop. Neurologists certainly have knowledge of some of the workings of the brain and they make speculations about consciousness. A similar situation arises in cosmology. We know a certain amount about the structure of the universe but the reason for its existence, if there is a reason, remains a matter of pure speculation.

Although sometimes denied by certain religious authorities and writers, cosmology is still fundamental with respect to religion. In lectures on the subject to various audiences and in the discussions following, the question of 'God' inevitably arises: hence the above-mentioned credibility given to the religious opinions of scientists who make cosmology their speciality. For example, the views of Stephen Hawking on religion (he appears to be an atheist) are listened to with far greater respect than those of a plumber or an electrician, although he is no more an authority on the fundamental question of the existence of a Supreme Being than the said artisan is. He can use his fine mathematical intellect to voice certain speculations regarding the origin of the universe and hence the necessity or sufficiency of a Creator, but they are speculations only. What mathematical cosmologists such as Hawking, Alan Guth and Smolin etc. can do is to use mathematics to inform their speculations regarding the structure, history and future of the universe. This does give credibility since speculation becomes fact if confirmed by observation. If denied by observation it becomes defunct. If observation is impossible, the validity of such speculation rests upon the balance of probability. Regarding the existence of God, there is disagreement among the academic community as to what the probability for His existence is. Among the devout, His existence is taken as read, as is His non-existence among confirmed atheists. Much of what this book attempts to do is to give an impartial account of the ideas that some of the scientists, theologians and religious writers have on this subject. Some scientists are indeed believers; some are atheists, but most are agnostic and tend to shy away from the subject of religion; whereas theologians, who are of course believers, do sometimes tend to concern themselves with scientific ideas. I have never come across an atheist theologian although the thought is an interesting one.

The Copernican Principle Appears to Invalidate the Western Religions

We shall see that in the balance of probability, modern cosmology appears to invalidate the eschatological (the last things, death, heaven and hell, etc.) aspects of the standard 'Western Religions',

Judaism Christianity and Islam. Whether it invalidates their associated ethics is another matter. In general, codes of ethical conduct are common to all religions and even atheists implicitly accept them. Ethics can therefore be postulated separately from any specific religion. The argument for their acceptance as objective values is often closely interwoven with the argument for Deism, the existence of a Supreme Being.

The probable invalidity of the Western religious eschatology rests upon the Copernican Principle, discussed further in the following chapter. This states that there is nothing special about our position or existence within the universe. Of course, the Copernican Principle itself is an assumption. It is however an eminently reasonable assumption. Observations have shown that the universe appears to have the same basic structure throughout space though not throughout time (see Chapter Two). The laws of physics seem to be independent of space and time. Since the laws of biology are based upon the laws of physics, life throughout the universe should have the same carbon-based structure as life on our planet (see Chapter Two). Some of these alien life-forms could either match or exceed us in intelligence. Astronomers consider the probability of the emergence of highly intelligent life on a planet to be very small. Even events with very small probabilities, however, become significant when the total number of events is vast. For instance, the probability of winning a large sum of money on the national lottery is approximately 14,000,000 to 1, but about a 100 people win it every year. In a similar fashion, the emergence of intelligent life among many billions and billions of planets although sparse should be both ubiquitous and significant. If the universe were infinite in extent then, despite their sparseness, there would be an infinite number of planets bearing intelligent life.

Some Religious and Atheistic Reactions to the Copernican Principle

These assumptions rely upon the theory of probability and the use of statistics. Politicians and others can easily abuse statistics to prove a point. Even scientists can engineer statistics to confirm their theories, but the honest use of statistics can be very informative, as we shall see in Chapter Six. The concept of the ubiquity of intelligent life throughout the universe does not stop some religious authorities from attempting to reject the Copernican Principle. This rejection is really a form of special pleading. The thoughts of the Rev David Wilkinson centre upon this rejection. His book *Alone in the Universe* is discussed in Chapter Two. C S Lewis in a small volume entitled *God in the Dock* points out that in Ptolemy's *Almagest*, compiled about AD140, the earth is described as having no appreciable size compared to the distance of the stars and must be considered as a mathematical point. Lewis thus contends that the pre-Copernican ancients were just as aware of the size of the universe as modern cosmologists but did not consider that this invalidated their religious beliefs. Why then, should it invalidate ours? This argument is rather ingenuous. The Copernican Principle takes into account not only the size of the universe, but its large-scale homogeneity and isotropy. The fact that for Ptolemy the earth forms a fixed point at the centre of the universe with the heavenly bodies in concentric spheres around it makes us very special indeed.

Professor Peacock, an authority on aerodynamics and a Christian, discusses modern cosmology in his book *A Brief History of Eternity*. This purports to be a considered response to Stephen Hawking's *A Brief History of Time*. Peacock looks at cosmology from a Christian point of view. He presents the Deistic argument from design very succinctly but fails to adapt it to the Christian doctrine. He also employs special pleading in his evolutionary argument. He claims that if evolution was the result of chance mutations and natural selection then we should have many more intermediate species, including that of 'near man'. S Wright gave an answer to this as long ago as 1932 in a paper on mutation and selection in evolution. He introduced the concept of a space of possible genotypes, whereby each one has a *fitness value* and the distribution of fitness values over the space of possible genotypes constitutes a *fitness landscape*. Depending upon geographical and environmental effects, this landscape consists of mountains of high fitness and valleys of low fitness. The peaks constitute the existence of the present genotypes and the valleys the possible but non-existent intermediate ones. Stuart Kauffman has used this concept in his work on self-organisation and selection in evolution described in Chapter Two. Peacock's argument really rests upon his faith. Having recruited selected great pre-twentieth-century scientists such as Sir Isaac Newton, Clerk-Maxwell, Faraday, Lord Kelvin, Pascal and, in particular Galileo as fellow Christian believers, he presents an emotional appeal for the acceptance of the truth of Christianity This runs into two problems. Firstly, as we have stated, eminent scientists do not necessarily have a greater knowledge of religion or certainty of faith than anyone else. Secondly, although postulated by Giordano Bruno in the sixteenth century, the Copernican Principle was not fully recognised until the confirmation of the extent and homogeneity of the universe in the twentieth (see the section 'Conformation of the Copernican Principle' and Chapter One).

Albert Einstein referred to it as the 'Cosmological Principle' and used it in the derivation of his relativistic cosmology. The majority of modern observational cosmologists now accept it as the basis for their calculations.

Special and General Relativity

Without going into the rather intricate mathematical details required for a full explanation, Einstein's theories are based upon the fact that the ultimate speed possible through space in the universe is that of light (electro-magnetic radiation) in a true vacuum. The Special Theory leads to what is known as time dilation (stretching) and mass increase in any frame (an aeroplane, for example) that is moving at a constant velocity with respect to an observer (on the ground, say). In other words, when measured by the ground observer, one second of time in the aeroplane would be slightly longer than one second of time is on the ground. This only becomes significant at speeds approaching that of light, which no aeroplane can possibly attain. Thus, the time dilation and mass increase is not normally noticed. The General Theory of Relativity extends the process to accelerating frames including gravity. This is presented in terms of Einstein's field equations, which except in certain simple cases, involve very difficult calculations.

Confirmation of the Copernican Principle

Until about the time that Einstein postulated his 'Cosmological Principle', it still seemed possible to consider man as the main purpose of creation. Copernicus started a trend by showing that the earth revolved around the sun, not the sun around the earth. Universal homogeneity was not confirmed observationally until the invention of the spectroscope (see Chapter Two) in 1850. This was because the stars, although differing in mass, temperature and age, were shown by the spectroscope to consist of the same gases and elements as the sun. In fact, the sun appeared to be an average star having a certain mass and temperature, known to astronomers as a G2V spectral class star, of which there are about ten billion in our galaxy. Finally, in the twentieth century it was discovered that there were millions of galaxies made up of stars similar to those in our own galaxy, hence the invocation by Einstein of the 'Cosmological or Copernican Principle'. It has received further confirmation in the last decade by the discovery that planetary systems seem to be a common accompaniment to stars.

The probable scientific invalidity of the more fundamentalist aspects of the Western Religions does not necessarily imply the invalidity of God. Some atheist scholars and authors take special pleading in the opposite direction. Professor Richard Dawkins, the

Albert Einstein

well-known biologist, claims that the biological process of natural selection invalidates the concept of a conscious Designer. Man is the result of pure chance, a lucky accident of the evolutionary process. This is also a way of rejecting the Copernican Principle. 'Pure chance' itself is governed by the laws of probability, which tell us, if the principle holds, that man or his equivalent is an inevitable product of the universe. Professor Dennett, the distinguished philosopher would extend Darwin's idea of evolution by natural selection to cosmology itself. He does this with reference to the cosmological speculations of Lee Smolin, Professor of Physics at Pennsylvania State University. A full discussion of these ideas and speculations is given in Chapter Six.

A Digression on Certain Mathematical Concepts

Although hardly any mathematics are used in this book it is as well to be aware of two generally used terms that have a mathematical basis. The term 'space' is normally accepted as the physical space that contains our universe and us. In mathematics, 'space' is often used to denote an abstract concept containing measurable or countable elements. This includes of course a space corresponding to the above-mentioned physical space with the relative position of an object as a measurable element. There are, however, many other mathematical spaces. For example, consider a space corresponding to temperature and pressure. Here the object would be placed in this space with respect to its temperature and pressure as measurable elements rather than its position. This could easily be shown by means of a graph with temperature as one of the axis and pressure as the other. Then there is the term 'dimension'. Many writers often use this as if it had a real physical meaning. They blithely talk of the fourth and fifth dimensions, etc., as if they were magic realms beyond our ken. In fact, scientifically speaking, a dimension is an abstract mathematical concept used to describe the number of measurable elements in a mathematical space that are completely independent of each other. For instance, if there are three such elements then such a space would correspond to real physical space since we can measure the relative position of an object in three independent ways. Along, Across and Up/Down from a specified origin. Hence, we have a space of three dimensions. We cannot conceive of a real physical space of four or more dimensions with four or more rulers all mutually at right-angles. We can easily have such a space in mathematics but to be compatible with physics the fourth dimension would have to be some other independent quantity like time or temperature or pressure. If we include time as an independent quantity then we have a real physical space called space-time. Cosmologists in calculations involving Einstein's Theory of Relativity use this. If we also include a further independent quantity such as temperature or pressure for example, then we have a space corresponding to five dimensions, and so on. What it appears we cannot have is directional physical space of more or less than three dimensions. Even the thinnest strand must have some breadth and depth as well as length. Even the flattest pancake must have some height as well as area. Certain solutions to problems in particle physics require a ten-dimensional space-time. This is a mathematical solution to a problem in string theory and requires an altogether more profound understanding of the theory than we have now. According to the string theory specialist Edward Witten, at the incredibly small lengths involved it may not make sense to talk about space and time at all.

This digression on the real meaning of 'dimension' is meant to alert the reader to the misuse of the word, particularly by religious apologists. The theologian Willem Drees, for example, talks about God existing in another spatial dimension in which our space-time is embedded (see Chapter Four). This sounds like mathematics but is really mysticism. What he really means is that God exists in some mystic realm beyond and above our knowledge. Such an idea has informed religious thinkers through the ages. It is not an idea lacking in religious credibility but should not be disguised as science or mathematics.

CHAPTER ONE

The Copernican Principle

WHY SHOULD WE BE SO SPECIAL?

In the final act of *King Lear*, the old king, stricken with grief, looks down on his dead daughter Cordelia and exclaims, 'Why should a dog, a horse, a rat have life, and thou no breath at all?'

This question could not occur to a dog, a horse or a rat. Indeed, it could not occur to any living thing in this world other than a human being. The questioning of purpose is unique to humankind and separates us in a very special way from all other known forms of life.

Whether or not this questioning of life's purpose has any validity or not, man still seems to be the only creature on the planet that does not take the universe for granted. All life-forms appear to be an integrated part of the universe. The more highly developed mammals, although conscious, showing intelligence and curiosity, do not seem to possess self-consciousness. Man alone, it seems, is able to distinguish himself in an objective manner from the universe in which he lives. How did this come about and what, if anything is its significance? From an evolutionary point of view this could be a result of the development of the brain and thus of consciousness. If so, it could be a side-effect since neither consciousness nor awareness of the universe is necessary for survival. Think of plant life, for example. Both Dawkins the biologist and Dennett the philosopher would embrace this idea, as would most contemporary biologists. There is a different idea, held by the proponents of religion; that man's unique place, not only on this planet but also in the universe as a whole, is a result of conscious design by a supreme being. Dennett amusingly refers to such proponents as hanging their arguments on skyhooks. A skyhook is defined by the *Oxford English Dictionary* as 'an imaginary contrivance for the attachment to the sky; an imaginary means of suspension in the sky'. This is a very clever use of rhetoric since not only does it imply that the arguments themselves are nonsense but it lends a pejorative overtone to anyone making them. Not all such arguments are hung on skyhooks. Some of them, from the arena of modern cosmology, can be quite convincing, as we shall see later. Let us first look at the progress made in cosmology and its effect upon the religious ideas through the ages.

The Pre and Post Copernican Eras in Cosmology and Religion

The development of Western religion, extensively dealt with in Richard Tarnas's magnificent book *The Passion of the Western Mind* was a long, arduous and difficult process, engaging some of the greatest minds of the past. In effect, it can be divided into two eras: pre- and post-Copernican. In the pre-Copernican era, the earth and hence humankind was at the centre of the universe. In the post-Copernican era, the earth had been expelled from its central position and the importance of humanity reduced accordingly. All the main religions originated in the pre-Copernican era and in essence are still pre-Copernican. This does not necessarily imply that all aspects of religion are invalid, in particular, those dealing with ethics, the existence of archetypal forms and objective values. It does, however, invalidate many basic concepts of the three main Western Religions, Judaism, Christianity and to a lesser extent Islam. Since the Eastern religions of Buddhism and Hinduism are less specific in their cosmology, they have been less affected. Let us briefly examine some of the ideas and attitudes that led to the post-Copernican world and the final establishment of the Copernican Principle.

The Formation of Religious and Cosmological Concepts

The mental transition from animal consciousness to human sentience and self-consciousness remains unexplained. According to Steven Rose in his book *The Conscious Brain*, it is the inevitable consequence of the development of increasingly flexible and modifiable behavioural performance, achieved by increasing the size of the brain and the complexity of the possible interactions of its components. This is a reasonable assumption, but it does not really explain the leap from consciousness to self-consciousness and thus acquiring the ability to contemplate the universe in an impartial manner. Possibly, the human ability to engage in precise communication by speech could have played an important part in this transition. Richard Dawkins in his book *Unweaving the Rainbow* suggests that hunting and mastering the ability to throw projectiles at a target may also have contributed. On the other hand, Gerald Schroeder in *Genesis and the Big Bang* and *The Science of God* considers that it was divine intervention.

Whatever the mechanics behind such a transition, it certainly took place at some time in the history of *Homo sapiens* or his antecedents. At this stage, man would have examined his surroundings and in doing so would visualise the earth as a vast, undiscovered, unexplored mystery. Together with the sky, this was considered the total universe. The sky appeared as a two-dimensional vault in which were implanted the stars and through which the sun and moon traversed daily. The change in the positions of the heavenly bodies would eventually have been seen to correspond with the annual change of seasons. It would have been noted that seasonal migrations of various birds and animals could be predicted by observing such changes. In the coastal regions, it could soon be seen that the tides would rise and fall according to the positions of the sun and moon. At various times, frightening events such as eclipses of the sun or moon, or the appearance of comets would have taken place. Those who carried out these observations thus became important members of society, who could advise on tribal movements for hunter-gatherers and, later on, when society became agricultural, on crop-planting and harvesting.

By dint of careful and painstaking recording throughout the seasonal year, these first observers charted the movements of the heavenly bodies, which were found to have regular daily and annual motions, exceptions being the wandering stars (planets) which would sometimes double-back on their tracks. From these observations throughout the cycle of the seasons, there arose a basic belief in the idea of a harmonious cosmos. Such harmony, it was thought, could only arise by virtue of a deliberate creation. Such an idea was reinforced by man's overwhelming sense of the numinous, which implies the existence of something other than our physical world (see Chapter Seven), something holy or divine or sometimes evil and terrifying. Man by means of his imaginative faculty has experienced it in different forms. The numinous manifests itself in seemingly irrational ways: in fear of the dead for instance, surely, the most harmless of creatures? In the ancient world, it could be found in the form of the Earth Goddess personifying fertility to the agricultural communities of the Neolithic age. She had various names: Inana in Sumeria, Anat in Canaan, Ishtar in Babylon, Isis in Egypt, Aphrodite in ancient Greece and Venus in Rome. Man's imagination was further affected by the numinous mystery of creation. This gave rise to many independent myths of the creation of the world.

In all human societies, including the Chinese and the Aztec, these creation myths corresponded to a belief in a supreme spiritual haven populated by divine and fantastic beings responsible for the vagaries of human fate. The study of comparative creation myths is known as cosmogony, from the Greek meaning 'world birth'.

In a parallel with modern quantum cosmology, the Chinese considered that in the beginning an atom was formed from nothingness. In the course of time it splits into male and female principals, which themselves split into two. From these four elements springs a being, which in turn is broken up to form the constituted universe, while the worms from its decomposing body become humans. The Chinese always adopted a holistic attitude. They considered that there was always a connection between human actions and the behaviour of the heavens. Thus, they developed an astrological system, which they observe to this day, although now invalidated by modern science. The Hindu first book of the *Vishnu Purana* refers to Brahma (God) as existing in the forms of spirit and time. Then followed two other forms, crude matter and visible substance, which became the causes of creation, preservation and destruction. An ancient Egyptian myth describes Osiris as the very essence of primeval matter and the source of all creation. The Aztecs held the sun to be the source of all material force and the gods the holders of fate. The sun was a semi-liquid mass designated the Water-Sun. This was identified with the Tlalocs, the mountain gods of rain and fertility. The mountains were described as great vessels filled with water requiring the sacrifice of children whose tears brought rain from the Tlalocs. In ancient Peru, the Incas described all things emanating from Pachacamac the Universal Spirit from whom proceeded all other animals and plants on earth. The American Indians held that at first there were many self-existent divinities who existed unchanged through untold times in perfect concord. After this long period, however, character evolved and with it differences and rivalries, thus bringing conflict into the universe. In Assyrian inscriptions we find recorded the Chaldeo-Babylonian idea of an evolution of the universe out of the primeval flood and of the animal creation of earth and sea. In fact, these inscriptions show that in the ancient religions of Babylon and Chaldea there existed a narrative of the creation, the Enuma Elish, which in its most important features must have been the source of that incorporated in the Torah in the chapter of Genesis. The story was symbolic of the great mystery of the creation of the world. It was not intended as the literal truth.

In this Babylonian epic, there was no idea of creation from nothing. This was a much later philosophical development. In the beginning is a divine waste, liquid and all-encompassing, without boundary or definition. Eventually three gods arise from the primeval waste. Apsu (the abyss), his wife Tiamat (the sea) and Mummu (the Womb of chaos). Further gods emerge from these first gods by emanation, that is, from substances formed by the first gods from their own essence. First come Lahmu and Lahamn (silt). Then come Ansher and Kishar (the furthest reaches of sea and sky); and finally Anu (the heavens) and Ea (the earth). These younger and more dynamic gods rebel against their parents, symbolising the eternal conflict within nature. Ea conquers Apsu and Mummu but is powerless against Tiamat who creates a new consort, Kingu and produces a brood of monsters for her defence. But Ea has a magnificent child, Marduk the great God of the Sun. He promises to fight and overthrow Tiamat provided he becomes the ruler of the gods. After an epic battle, Marduk manages to slay Tiamat and creates a new world by splitting her body in two to form the vault of the sky and the world of men. He then declaims the laws of nature to achieve order in the world. Finally, he creates man by killing Kingu and mixing his divine blood with the dust of the earth. In this way, it is shown that man shares in a very limited way the divinity of the gods.

The biblical God in Genesis also creates the world from an unformed deep over which the darkness reigned. Again, he forms man from the dust of the earth in his own divine image. To the early Hebrews, this God is not at first the only god. He is Jehovah Saboath, a warrior god of the mountains and dwells among a pantheon of rival gods. He is, however, greater than any of them and requires total devotion if he is to ensure victory and triumph in the endless tribal warfare that is a feature of the early history of the Middle East.

Monotheism and the Greek Enlightenment

The belief of the early Israelites in the supremacy of their war god of the mountains, Jehovah, over all the gods of their rival tribes finally took the form of monotheism. The rival gods were deemed false and hence non-existent, leaving Jehovah as the one true God of the universe. This belief is now the basic tenet of the three major Western Religions and forms the basis of modern philosophical disputes concerning the existence of a Creator.

The first modern concept of the universe came not from the monotheistic Jews but from the Polytheistic Greeks. In 585BC, an eclipse of the sun took place. The Greek philosopher Thales had accurately predicted this eclipse, which marks the beginning of that most remarkable period in history, the ancient Greek enlightenment (600BC to AD400). These Greeks discovered science, philosophy and mathematics. They speculated on the nature of the universe around them. Pythagoras was the first to introduce mathematics in the form of demonstrative deductive argument, in about 535BC. He stated that 'all things are numbers', i.e. that the universe could be interpreted in terms of mathematics. If we extend the idea of number to include incommensurables such as π or $\sqrt{2}$ this becomes a most interesting concept, (which we will discuss in Chapter Five on 'Boundaries'). He also commented, as we shall see later, on the idea of a moving earth. The problem of incommensurables persuaded the Greeks to treat geometry independently from arithmetic, a task perfected by Euclid. It was not until Descartes in the seventeenth century that the two were effectively combined.

The Ionian philosophers Anaximander and Anaximenes wrought the concept of gradualism. They conceived the visible universe as a result of the process of evolution; indeed Democritus even introduces the rather modern idea of the atomic structure of matter. Epicures, a follower of Democritus, considered that this physical world was the only form of existence and that the gods were either irrelevant or illusory. We therefore have to make the best of things and strive for maximum happiness. His views have come down to us from the writings of the Roman poet Lucretius.

As an example of their scientific method of reasoning, consider how the following observations by travellers and astronomers led to a general acceptance of the sphericity of the earth:

1   Northbound travellers observe hitherto unseen stars appearing over the northern horizon while other stars disappear below the southern horizon. Southbound travellers observe the opposite effect. The only sensible explanation being that as the horizon had tipped to the north or south respectively, the travellers must be moving over a curved surface.

2   The shape of the earth's shadow during a lunar eclipse shows that this surface is a sphere, since only a sphere will always cast a round shadow.

3   A curious use of circumstantial evidence involved reasoning that as elephants were to be found in both the east (India) and the west (Morocco) then these two places could not be that far apart on a spherical earth. Considering the limitation on both the speed and distance of travel at the time it was an understandable mistake.

The Moving Earth

The ancient Greeks considered not only the rotundity but also the movement of our planet feasible. Philolaus first postulated a theory in the fifth century BC, of the movement of the planets and the earth, as well as the sun and the moon, about a central fire, with the earth rotating about its own axis in order to hide the central fire from the inhabitants of the known earth.

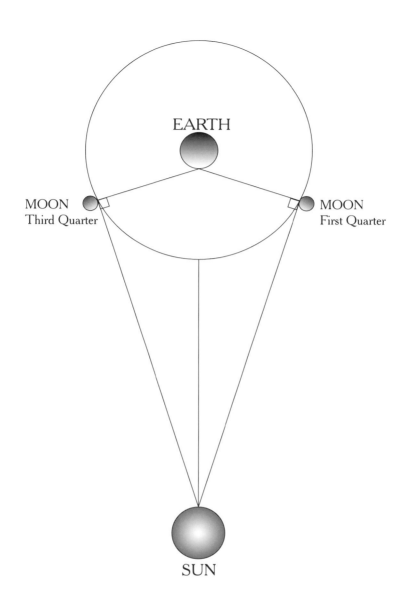

DIAGRAM ONE

The Method of Aristarchus

In about 300BC, Aristarchus of Samos, although he had no telescopes to assist him, made a conjecture from observing a solar eclipse that the sun must be further from the earth than the moon. He then reasoned that assuming the moon at its quarter-phases subtended a right-angle with respect to the earth and sun, he could find the distance of the sun from the earth in terms of the moon's distance. By trying to establish the exact time from the first to the third quarters of the moon and comparing that to the time taken from the third back to the first quarter, he calculated using direct proportion, the angle between the first quarter, the earth and the third quarter (see Diagram 1). Then using plane geometry, he estimated that the sun was some twenty times more distant from the earth than the moon. By observation of the earth's shadow during a lunar eclipse he also deduced that the moon's diameter was about three-eighths that of the earth and hence that the sun's diameter was about seven times that of the earth. This led him to a daring new theory that the earth revolved around the sun – rather than the sun about the earth. Modern calculations show that the sun is about four hundred times more distant than the moon but considering the observational limitations of the time it was a worthy scientific effort. It is now considered that the task of calculating the exact time between the moon's quarters is beyond our ability even with modern technology.

The result of such effort did not do Aristarchus any good. Cleanthes the stoic philosopher demanded that Aristarchus be indicted for blasphemy, since to displace the earth from the centre of the universe must lead to a breakdown of moral standards. Such a religious reaction to the heliocentric theory was to be duplicated and extended 1,900 years later by the Christian Church.

Plato's Theory of Forms

One of the most important and influential theories to arise from the Greek enlightenment was the theory of archetypal forms. This has been a source of dispute from 400BC to the present day. The

Plato and Aristotle

theory has great bearing upon the argument for a Designer universe and is employed to this end by many theistic apologists.

Plato's 'Theory of Forms' is a development of Socrates' 'Doctrine of Absolute Standards'. He maintains that there exists a world of patterns or models for things belonging to the physical universe that we experience. The importance he places upon these 'Forms' concerns the fact that they are primary objective constructs, both timeless and essential. Everything in our physical universe is the concrete expression of a universal archetype. Thus we have the absolute values of justice, beauty, virtue, etc., which form the basics of ethics. Without them, Plato believed that we would descend into a dangerous state of amoral relativism. Not only abstract values possess archetypes. All concrete constructs on earth have them. For example, the word 'horse' means an ideal horse, 'the horse' created by God. Particular horses partake of its nature but imperfectly. Because of their imperfections, there can be many horses but only the 'ideal horse' is real. Particular horses are only apparent to us. The concept of evolutionary development would seem to make such archetypes for the concrete unlikely. Those for abstractions, especially the independent existence of mathematics, could still be a matter of dispute.

Aristotle, his former student, further developed Plato's ideas. He considered that concrete archetypes were only a matter of nomenclature. He called them universals, but distinguished between form and matter. He said that it is in virtue of the form that matter becomes definite. In other words, an object must be bounded and the boundary is the form – an idea explored in Chapter Five.

In addition to philosophy, Aristotle wrote two books called *Physics* and *On the Heavens*. These dominated science until the beginning of the seventeenth century when Galileo appeared on the scene.

Aristotle considered that the source of all motion is 'Will'. On earth, it is the will of living forms and in the heavens the will of the supreme God, who is himself the unmoved mover. He also considered things below the moon to be corruptible and subject to generation and decay. Above the moon, everything is ungenerated and indestructible. The earth is spherical and at the centre of the universe. The heavens are perfectly spherical and the upper regions are more divine than the lower. The motions of these heavenly bodies are due to those of the celestial spheres to which they are attached.

The Platonic theory of forms had a profound influence on both Christianity and Islam. St Augustine himself agreed that this theory provided a firm basis for human knowledge. In addition, he considered that a doctrine of creation was needed to explain the construction of the concrete structures in the universe that mirrored these ideal forms. He thence argued that the ideas of Plato could be fulfilled by the Judaeo-Christian revelation of almighty God.

Realists and Nominalists

This theory formed the basis of the school of philosophy, which considered the archetypes to be the true reality; hence, it was referred to as the Realist school. William of Ockham founded an opposing school in the fourteenth century. Following Aristotle, he considered that Plato's Universal Forms are purely constructs of the human mind and that nothing exists except individual beings and objects to which we give appropriate names. This school was thus designated Nominalist. He claimed that concrete experience is the basis of human knowledge. He denied the human ability to deduce any facts about God. Anything known about Him is the result of revelation and faith. The truth of the Christian revelation is beyond doubt and cannot be arrived at by argument or reason. Thus, he both opposed and supported a secularist concept.

Scientists throughout the ages have usefully applied his famous dictum known as 'Ockham's Razor', which implies that the simplest explanation of a phenomenon is usually the correct one.

The rise of the Roman Empire and its conquest of Greece caused a diminution of scientific activity through the emphasis on commercial and military success. In the final centuries of the Roman rule, corruption, decadence and barbarian invasion finally ended classical civilisation, culminating in the closing of the academy in Athens by the Emperor Justinian in AD529. A few Christian monastic orders and Islamic scholars now carried the torch through the dark ages AD600 to AD1000 whereby much of Classical Hellenism was preserved.

The Islamic Contention

In Islam the famous Muslim thinker and philosopher Abu Hamin al-Ghazzali (1058–1111) gravitated to the Sufi mystics after studying the rational beliefs and ideas of an Islamic pragmatic philosophy known as the Falsafah. He gave as his reason the fact that although the Falsafah was excellent for observable phenomena such as astronomy, it could not deal with the concept of God. For this, the mystical practices of the Sufis were necessary. He put forward a creed based on the ancient idea of Plato's archetypal forms. These exist in a world superior to and beyond the known physical universe. This spiritual world is mentioned in both the Koran and the Bible. Mankind belongs in both worlds because God has fashioned him in the divine image.

In the Muslim world in the tenth century, a group of scholars designated the 'Ikhwan' believed in instantaneous creation rather than in the eternity of the world postulated by another group (the 'Dahriyun').

According to the Ikhwan God created the first four universal beings instantaneously in a series of effusions. The other beings were brought into existence by the Universal Soul acting with the permission of Allah the most high. They claim that the relation of the world to Allah is like the word in relation to him who speaks it, like light or heat to the lantern, the sun to the earth, or numbers to the number ONE. The word, light, heat and number exist by and through their respective sources without which they could neither exist nor persist in being. Allah thus determines the existence of the world.

The Universal Soul has only two causes, the efficient one being God and the formal one the intellect. It receives from the intellect all the virtues, forms and positive qualities and transmits them in turn to the whole universe. The Universal Soul is to the universe what the human soul is to the human body. Its field of action lies in the geocentric cosmos, which has the earth standing stationary at the centre with nine concentric spheres around it. It is the prime mover that makes the sphere of fixed stars perform its diurnal motion. All the bodies in the universe are like tools in the hand of the Universal Soul. It performs all actions through them in the same way that a carpenter uses tools for various ends. All change in the universe is therefore directed by its soul, which dominates the universe. It will be seen from the above that in cosmology they follow the system of Ptolemy (see Introduction, p8).

The Muslims were not ignorant of the idea of the moving earth even in the tenth century. One of their most learned scholars and scientists was al-Biruni. He was born in AD973 in Khiva in Uzbek. He lived most of his life in Ghanzna, Syria where he died in AD1051.

He accepts the concept of '*creation ex nihilo*' and rejects the eternity of the world. He considers creation as a manifestation of the power of the Creator. He accepts the scriptures for creation but regards the book of Genesis as symbolic. For example, the sun and moon were not brought into existence until the fourth day; hence, the first three '*days*' could refer to unknown periods of time. Unlike most modern scientists, he does not believe in the uniformity of the constants of nature. He thinks that certain orders of existence belong to certain times. He believes in a past '*Golden Age*' of mankind. He was an authority on both astronomy and astrology, which in the Muslim world were combined as a single discipline. He was aware of the heliocentric theory of Aristarchus. In his travels in India, it seems, he found such a theory taught by certain sages that he met. He remained neutral with respect to the geocentric or heliocentric concept. He considered that both theories could equally well explain all the appearances on the astronomical chart.

He eventually favoured the geocentric explanation because his calculations of the speed of the earth's rotation seemed to him to be too excessive to conform to terrestrial conditions.

It is informative to note that his reason for accepting the geocentric concept was purely scientific and not in any way religious. Unlike the apocalyptic Christian religion, Islam did not condemn the use of scientific reason to investigate the world, hence the very high standard of Muslim scholarship sustained throughout the dark ages of Europe.

Christian Judaic Cosmology

The cosmology in the Christian world followed the Jewish Torah in the chapter Genesis, the Torah itself becoming the first five books of the Bible under the Christian nomenclature of the Old Testament. This cosmology of Genesis begins with a 'Creator' forming the universe with his hands or his breath (word). In general, it was thought that this Creator or God created everything from nothing, *'creation ex nihilo'*, as opposed to the Platonic view of creation, which believed in the pre-existence of matter. The time taken for this creation was generally accepted by the monotheistic believers to be six days as stated in the Bible, although interestingly enough in the light of modern theory, the Jewish philosopher Philo postulated an instantaneous creation, but all for our convenience. This subject is discussed more fully in Chapter Two.

The early Christian fathers assumed that the movement of the heavenly bodies was the task of angelic beings. They were constantly employed, pulling and pushing the sun, moon and stars around the heavens as well as periodically opening the window of heaven to ensure rainfall. All this was being undertaken in addition to their other heavenly duties. The originator of this school of cosmology was a sixth-century monk, Cosmos Indicapleustes. He believed in a flat earth with a flat heaven above containing a huge water tank. St Philastrius, in his treatise on heresies, pronounced it a heresy to deny that the stars are 'brought out by God from his treasure house and hung in the sky every evening'. Any other view he declared 'false to the Catholic faith'.

St Isadore, the leader of orthodox belief in the seventh century, claimed that because of the fall of man, both the sun and the moon shine with a feebler light but when the world is fully redeemed, they will shine again in all their early splendour. In spite of these theological pronouncements, the evolution of scientific thought culminated in the '*Ptolemaic theory*' the main ingredient being the geocentric doctrine that the earth is at the centre of the universe and all the other heavenly bodies revolve about it. This theory had come from the ancient world into Christianity. St Clement of Alexandria showed that in the Jewish tabernacle, the altar was a symbol of the earth placed in the middle of the universe. Thus, the theory was theologically acceptable.

The real divide between science and religion originated with the Heliocentric Theory. As we have seen, Aristarchus of Samos promulgated this in ancient times. In the fifth century, Martianus Capella tentatively raised it, but it was not until the fifteenth century that the idea started to take hold, with the advent of Cardinal Nicholas de Cusa. It was his writings that gave rise to the heretical ideas of Giordano Bruno.

Nicholas de Cusa was ordained in AD1440 and became a bishop in AD1450 in Bressanone. His interests included mathematics and logic, especially the study of the infinite. He took the circle as the limit of a regular polygon with an infinite number of sides, thus pre-empting a method used in the integral calculus. He used this method to demonstrate how one can only approach truth but never reach it completely. He argued that man's knowledge of the universe was incomplete and that the search for truth is equivalent to the task of squaring the circle. In AD1444 he became interested in cosmology and postulated the following:

1   Every direction is relative to every other direction. (The first statement of relativity.)

2   The universe has no central point.

3   This means that nowhere in the universe is unique. (The first statement of non-uniqueness.)

4   The earth may not be stationary.

5   The universe will appear similar from all positions. (The first statement of the homogeneity of the universe.)

He later claimed that the earth moves round the sun and that the stars are other suns with planets, possibly inhabited, orbiting round them. The church looked upon these ideas as a form of scientific curiosity or paradox and they were not taken seriously at the time.

Finally, the heliocentric system was reintroduced in detail by the Pole, Nicolaus Copernicus (Mikolaj Koppernijk, in Polish) in 1530 in his famous book *De Revolutionibus Orbium Celestium*. It was published in 1542, the day of his death; a rather wise move in the light of what happened to his successors, who, among other things, embraced similar ideas: Galileo himself, forced to retract, and Giordano Bruno, who withdrew his original retraction and was hence burnt at the stake. In fact, Copernicus's publisher, Osiander wrote a grovelling preface asserting that the doctrine of the movement of the earth was merely a hypothesis and that it was lawful for an astronomer to indulge his imagination. This preface served its purpose. For the next fifty years or so, the church authorities considered it wise not to give the matter too much prominence. The fact that Copernicus still accepted the earth and sun as the centre of the universe and believed in the celestial sphere of fixed stars helped to calm the situation. In 1576, Thomas Digges proposed the theory that there was no such thing as the fixed sphere of the stars. He considered the heavens to be infinite but the sun and earth still unique at the heart of the cosmos.

The Challenge to the Church

Throughout Europe, these ideas of Aristarchus that Copernicus had resurrected were not considered a challenge to the current establishment. The Roman Catholic Church ostensibly accepted the argument put forth in Osiander's preface that they were theories or speculations. The church could counter them with its own arguments. When Galileo came on the scene with his observations and experiments, the whole intellectual climate was shaken. His astronomical observations, using the newly invented telescope, could not be so easily dismissed. He claimed the Copernican heliocentric theory not as a speculation but as a truth.

Although we may consider that the new enlightenment started with Galileo, he did not spring like Athena, fully armed from the forehead of Zeus. He had very illustrious antecedents. His methods were a development of the Nominalist philosophy introduced by William of Ockham. The assertion that existence is purely individualistic opened the way to scientific analysis of the physical world. Buridan and Oresme, two of the most original scientific precursors to Galileo, both worked in the Nominalist school in Paris. Their methods and ideas of practical experiment were followed by Galileo at an early stage and subsequently extended.

Galileo was born in 1564. He began his career as a medical student, but finding little interest in this subject, he turned to mathematics. Shortage of money prevented him from completing his university career but his exceptional ability at mathematics gained him the position of Professor of Mathematics and Astronomy at the University of Pisa in 1589. In 1592, he gained an even better position at the University of Padua where he remained until 1610. While at Padua he became famous as both a teacher and as Europe's foremost 'Scientific Investigator'.

He was not content with accepting the sacred doctrines of the Holy Scriptures or the authoritative philosophy of Aristotle. Following Buridan and Oresme, he carried out experiments to see if they were true. In many cases, he found that they were not. In particular, the one decisive result that he obtained was his observation of the fact that the planet Venus showed phases just like the moon. The observations were carried out using the telescope and showed that Venus revolved around the sun. This of course implied that the earth in its turn also revolved about the sun and was therefore not the centre of the universe as implicitly stated in the Holy Scriptures. He also discovered that Jupiter had its own set of moons and that the Milky Way consisted of thousands of stars when viewed through the telescope. All this led to powerful observational evidence for the confirmation of the heliocentric theory initiating what is now referred to as *The Copernican Revolution*.

The history of Galileo's conflict with the church is well known and is not really the subject of this book. What is important is the Copernican Revolution and the later founding of the 'Copernican Principle' which has come to have a far wider implication than the original idea of the earth revolving about the sun rather than the other way about. In 1609 Kepler published his investigation into the orbit of the planet Mars around the sun. Using observations taken with great diligence and accuracy by Tycho Brahe, Kepler deduced that the orbit of Mars was an ellipse with the sun at one of the foci. In 1621, Kepler had published *The Epitome of the Copernican Astronomy*. This book contained the information that not only Mars but also all the planets including earth had elliptical orbits around the sun. This book was immediately put on the Roman Index of Prohibited Books. It called into question the idea of the heavenly bodies being encased in celestial spheres, tending to confirm the theory of Thomas Digges mentioned previously.

It was not until the publication of Sir Isaac Newton's *Principia* in 1689 that the motions of the planets and consequently the other heavenly bodies were really understood. Although accepted in England at the time, it was fifty years before his gravitational theory was accepted on the continent of Europe. In 1704, Newton published his treatise on *Optics*. This established that white light is composite and that by passing a beam of sunlight through a prism it can be decomposed into different colours, its visible spectrum ranging from red to violet. The differences in colour correspond to the differences in the wavelength of the light, red being the longest and violet the shortest in the spectrum. Instead of a prism, it is possible to use a narrow slit called a diffraction grating to analyse the light into its respective wavelengths. In 1814, Joseph Fraunhofer carefully examined the sun's spectrum and discovered about 600 dark lines in it. Further examination showed the existence of various bright lines. In 1859, Gustav Kirchhoff showed that these lines are indicative of different substances, specific substances having specific lines characteristic of the substance in question. This discipline of spectroscopy made it possible to discover what substances the sun was made of. All the constituent elements in the sun were also known to exist on earth, except helium, which was eventually found in 1895. In the latter half of the nineteenth century, spectroscopic observations of the stars showed that the same elements were found in the stars, thus establishing the laws of physics to be universal. In addition to this, it was the discovery of our galaxy, and later in the twentieth century, the existence of many external galaxies (see Chapter Two), that led to the confirmation of the Copernican Principle.

It has been remarked that the Copernican or 'Cosmological' Principle was first used by Einstein as an assumption for the solution of his field equations in relativistic cosmology, with respect to the distribution of matter and energy in the universe. It is invoked as the basis of the homogeneity and isotropy of the universe. By this, we mean that irrespective of an observer's position in the universe, not only will it present a similar appearance but it will also consist of the same structural elements. As Copernicus showed that there was nothing special about our place within the solar system, so further observations showed that there was nothing special about the solar system's place within the galaxy nor our galaxy's place within the observed universe. The majority of modern cosmologists now use it in their calculations.

This startling revision of the significance, or rather the insignificance, of our place within the observed universe could have sounded the death-knell of two of the three major Western Religions, Judaism and its offspring, Christianity. Islam being less anthropocentric in this respect would be less affected. The continuing survival of religion, not only through the Copernican but also through the Darwinian revolution, indicates a human desire for the psychological security of some external purposive concept. Whether this is a result of evolutionary factors, or deliberate creative design, or both, is at present a matter of debate.

The impact of the Reformation in the seventeenth century invoked a fiercely defensive reaction of the church with respect to the Holy Scriptures. It followed that its attitude to the heliocentric theory was highly condemnatory when Galileo at last invoked it as a truth. This applied not only to the Roman Catholic Church but to the Protestants as well. Both Martin Luther and John Calvin launched attacks on Copernicus stating that his theory was contrary to the Holy Scriptures. In this, the church was not wrong. It was contrary to the Holy Scriptures and Galileo's observations could to all intents and purposes have disposed of the Holy Scriptures as fiction. Why, if the cosmology of the religion was found wanting, should any other aspect of it be believed? Of course, this did not happen. The church was too powerful and it was for most people their main source of security. The prospect of death and the promise of immortality were strong factors in the church's favour, overriding the inconvenience of any evidence to the contrary. The consequent slow retreat of Western religion in the face of further scientific discoveries has been a tactical withdrawal, using the sophistry of the Judaeo-Christian apologists as a defence mechanism. The fundamentalists will have none of this and still rely upon the authority of the Holy Scriptures. Thus, there has arisen a rift in religious thinking between the fundamentalists and the secularists. This division can be seen in all three of the Western Religions. It has its origins in the Copernican theory and the scientific enlightenment originating with Galileo. Before

Copernicus, there was a consensus within the religions as to the primary importance and theological significance of mankind, although there were many differences and arguments as to the application of such orthodoxy. Atheism as opposed to rejection was almost unknown in the West although we do find a reference to true atheism in Psalm 14: 'The fool hath said in his heart there is no God.'

The Secular Implication

The nearest parallel to the orthodox secular rift in ancient times occurred in 175BC with the attempted Hellenisation of the Jews by the Seleucid monarch, Antiochus Epiphanes. From his point of view, this was a matter of economics rather than scientific discovery. Short of money for his wars, Epiphanes thought it would raise tax revenues. Hellenisation also involved a new critical approach to religion and a method very close to the modern scientific outlook. Some of the Jews thought that this would allow them to combine the new civilisation of Greece with the Jewish idea of a universal God. In general, the Greeks favoured a polytheistic religion, which did not recognise the absolute distinction between human and divine, that was the very basis of Judaism. The final straw was the intention of the Greeks to install a statue of Zeus in the holy temple in Jerusalem. This led to a fierce struggle between the Maccabees, who were orthodox Jews, against the Greeks and the Hellenised Jews, which ended with the victory of the Maccabees in 164BC.

The 'secular' religionists regard the moral basis of religion as providing the truest insight into the workings of humanity while the exploded basis of religious cosmology can be interpreted as myth or the early speculation of pre-scientific man. That there can be a certain justification for this view will be discussed later but it still leaves the uncomfortable assertion of Messianic prophecy, the Incarnation and the resurrection of the dead, all of which imply that the earth is the centre of the universe with respect to life and that man is the epitome of creation. Thomas Paine raised this

Thomas Paine

problem in his *Age of Reason in* 1793. He says: 'To believe that God created a plurality of worlds at least as numerous as what we call stars, renders the Christian system of faith at once little and ridiculous and scatters it in the mind like feathers in the air. The two beliefs cannot be held together in the same mind; and he who thinks that he believes in both has thought but little of either.'

To counter the problem raised by Thomas Paine there is a certain amount of 'special pleading' with regard to the scriptures and the Koran. For example, the Koran talks about the seven heavens, one above the other, and the stars being placed in the nearest heaven as lamps or missiles to drive away evil spirits:

> ' 3 Who has created the seven heavens one above the other; you can see no fault in the creation of the most Gracious. Then look again: 'Can you see any rifts?'
>
> 4 Then look again and yet again: your sight will return to you in a state of humiliation and worn out.
>
> 5 And indeed We have adorned the nearest heaven with lamps and We have made such lamps as missiles to drive away the devils and have prepared for them the torment of the blazing Fire.'
>
> (Surah 67 Surat Al-Mulk 3, 4, 5)

Although this quote seems to follow the standard Ptolemaic system, the Koran can also quote

> '47 With power did We construct the heaven. Verily, We are Able to extend the vastness of space thereof.'
>
> (Surah 51 Surat Adh-Dhariyat 47)

This could indicate the expansion of the universe.

In a similar fashion, the order of creation in Genesis (1 to 19) seems to be wrong, with the creation of light occurring before the creation of the sun and moon. If it were looked at in the frame of an observer on earth, it would make more sense, with the heavens becoming visible after the thinning of the dense cloud cover, etc. There are many more cases of such interpretations from holy writings, which serve to show that almost any idea can be confirmed by reference to such writings. This helps to explain the origin of the differing religious sects or divisions among all three of the Western monotheistic religions.

A further result of the Copernican revolution was to make atheism not only respectable but in many cases desirable. The French revolution, for instance, was instigated as a reaction against the monarchy and the church. The later establishment of Communism throughout a large part of the world rested upon Marxist economics and his claim that religion was '*the opium of the people*'. Marxism also insisted upon the deterministic inevitability of history with respect to the class struggle, in what was ironically, an almost Calvinistic version of atheism? Like Christianity, Marxism establishes a primary role for humankind in the universe, giving it a pre-Copernican overtone. That this theory has also exploded shows the danger of over-simplification in politics as well as cosmology.

The Eastern Impact

In the Eastern religions, the Copernican revolution had far less impact than it did in the west. The Vedas of Hinduism, for instance, express a lofty and mystical belief in one divine being that includes all knowledge and all nature within itself, a form of pantheism that can be adapted to the universe whatever its size and however it was formed. The later modifications of the religion into various forms of animalism and paganism had a purely local effect. One of these effects gave rise to a vigorous group of atheists in the fifth century BC. These were the Charvakas, a warrior caste who proclaimed that the whole system of priests, sacrifices and prayers was pure mumbo-jumbo and that the highest good is to strive for happiness, thus pre-empting the Greek Epicureans by two centuries.

In general, the Hindu belief in the transmigration of souls into various human or animal forms can fit in very conveniently with Darwinian evolution. Buddhism, an offshoot of ancient Hinduism, can also be easily adapted to modern cosmology. The scriptures of Buddhism, unlike the Bible and the Koran are not considered works of divine revelation. They are the recorded sermons, dialogues and addresses of Buddha during his teaching life. They set out a standard of conduct needed to reach the state of Buddhahood.

These teachings advocate a state of inactive perfect calm in which the restless spirit is at one with the universe. Since Buddhists believe that the universe is infinite in duration and extent, without a God or Creator, the Copernican Principle is easily incorporated into both their philosophy and religion.

In the next three chapters, we examine some of the features of the universe that appear to have displaced mankind from its central position so beloved of the western monotheistic religions, and at the same time look at some of the theistic arguments of their apologists.

Summary

This chapter examines the history of cosmology from the religious, philosophical and scientific points of view. It is pointed out that the three main 'Western' religions, Judaism Christianity and Islam originated in a pre-Copernican world and philosophically remain in that world. The Eastern religions, Hinduism, Buddhism, etc., are also pre-Copernican but being less anthropomorphic than the Western Religions were less affected by the Copernican revolution.

The early enlightenment of Classical Greece is discussed, with particular mention of Plato's archetypes and Aristotle's conception of the universe and God. These two philosophers' ideas polarised into the Realist and Nominalists schools.

The calculations of Aristarchus of Samos indicated the

revolution of the earth around the sun. Later ideas of the 'moving earth' by Nicholas de Cusa, preceded the calculations of Copernicus, which, when demonstrated by Galileo, ushered in the Copernican revolution. This in time evolved into the 'Copernican or Cosmological Principle' first employed by Einstein in his cosmological calculations. Many of the basic tenets of the three Western Religions appear to be rendered untenable by this principle, in spite of special pleading, with respect to both the Bible and the Koran.

Chapter Two

Space

Where does it all come from?

First, let us consider the extent of our universe. Galileo's observations extended our universe to contain thousands of stars, each one of which appeared to be equivalent to our sun. Following Johannes Kepler's calculations with Newton's formulation of the laws of dynamics and gravity, the motions of the heavenly bodies took on a logical precision. Our understanding of the observed orbits of the planets helped to present a more orderly picture of the universe without the help of angels.

Distance Measurements

The first reasonably accurate distance measurement to a heavenly body was made in 1671–73 by Jean Richer in Cayenne and Giovanni Dominic Cassini, Jean Picard and others in Paris. The observations were of the altitude of the planet Mars when it was in opposition to the sun. They were made simultaneously at an agreed time. Knowing the distance between Cayenne and Paris, the triangle Paris–Cayenne–Mars could be solved and the distance to Mars calculated (Diagram Two). They obtained a result of 83,000,000 kilometres, not far out from the modern value of 90 million kilometres. This type of measurement is known as measurement by parallax. It should be pointed out that the term *parallax of a*

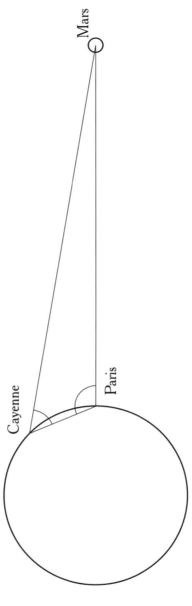

DIAGRAM TWO

Distance measurement of Mars by parallux,
1671

heavenly body (i.e. the sun, moon, or planet) refers to the angle between the lines joining the body to the observer and the centre of the earth. It is obvious that such an angle is greatest when the observer sees the body just rising or setting. It is then known as *horizontal parallax* (Diagram 3). Thus, distances to the moon and sun can be calculated in a similar fashion to that described above. In the particular case of the sun Cassini deduced from Richer's observations that its horizontal parallax was 9'·5 corresponding to a distance from the earth of 87,000,000 miles. The modern value is averaged at about 93,000,000 miles, so it was not that far out, considering the limitations of seventeenth-century technology.

This puts the sun at about 372 times the distance of the moon. From this, we can readily calculate the size of the sun. It is a ball of hot gas (plasma) about 330,000 times the mass and 1,000,000 times the volume of the earth. This vast structure, far surpassing anything that the ancients could imagine, is actually a very ordinary star. It is halfway through its lifetime of about ten billion years and has a surface temperature of around 6,000 degrees Celsius. The astronomers classify it as a type G2 dwarf star, the type referring to its temperature. It is made up of seventy-one per cent hydrogen and twenty-six per cent helium with three per cent of other elements. The light from the sun, travelling at 186,000 miles per second, takes on average 8 minutes and 19 seconds to reach the earth. Since the earth makes a slight elliptical orbit around the sun its distance and hence the light time will differ slightly from the average. Eight other planets join the earth with orbits around the sun. They are in order of distance from the sun: Mercury – 36,000,000 miles, Venus – 67,000,000 miles, earth – 93,000,000 miles, Mars – 141,000,000 miles, Jupiter – 484,000,000 miles, Saturn – 887,000,000 miles, Uranus – 1,784,000,000 miles, Neptune – 2,796,000,000 miles and Pluto – 3,668,000,000 miles. Between Mars and Jupiter, there are thousands of minor planets. Comets from distant parts of our solar system also orbit the sun in highly elliptical orbits. Most of the planets have moons orbiting them; Jupiter, for instance, has at least thirteen. The smallest planet is Mercury; about

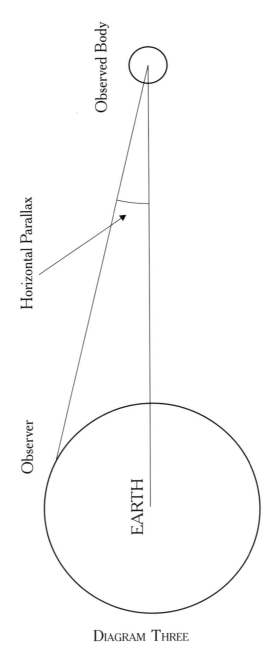

DIAGRAM THREE

The horizontal parallax

1/20 the size of earth and the largest is Jupiter, about 1,300 time the size of earth.

This whole solar system is but one of many within our galaxy known as the Milky Way. How many stars are there in our galaxy and how far away are they? Using telescopes with photographic plates, the parallaxes of the nearest stars are measured by their displacements against the background of more distant stars. This is accomplished by examining the photographs taken when the earth is at opposite sides of its orbit around the sun. The closest stars to our sun are the three that make up the triple system Alpha Centauri. They consist of the bright Alpha Centauri itself, which is a double star, and a faint star Proxima Centauri, which is slightly closer to us than the other two stars. Even from these closest stars it takes light over four years to reach the earth. This compares with the five and a half hours that light takes to reach us from the planet Pluto.

In 1750, Thomas Wright first suggested that the sun is a part of a large system of stars. In 1785, William Herschel published the results of star counts in 683 selected regions of the sky. He concluded that the sun was indeed part of an immense sidereal disc-shaped system. Using modern techniques, such as statistical studies of samples of the sky, ground based telescopes give an estimated 200 billion stars in our galaxy which has an approximate diameter of over 100,000 light years. It is calculated that about ten per cent of the stars are G-type or sun-like. If like the sun, they also have planetary systems that would give twenty billion possibilities of other earth-like planets existing in our galaxy.

The Probability of Extra-Terrestrial Civilisations

A speculative, and in principle, simple method of determining the number of contemporary advanced civilisations existing in our galaxy was put forward by Frank Drake at a conference on extra-terrestrial life held at the National Radio Astronomy Observatory in USA in November 1961. It consisted of the following probability calculation.

The probable number of contemporary advanced civilisations N, within the galaxy is equal to: –

$$N = (R^*) \times (fp) \times (ne) \times (fl) \times (fi) \times (fc) \times (L)$$

i.e. the mean rate of star formation within the galaxy (R^*), times the fraction of stars with planetary systems (fp), times the mean number of planets in each planetary system with environments favourable to the formation of life (ne), times the fraction of such favourable planets on which life does develop (fl), times the fraction of life bearing planets where intelligent life develops (fi), times the fraction of planets with advanced technology (fc) times the lifetime of the technical civilisation (L).

Unfortunately, not all of these quantities are known so a certain amount of speculation is necessary. A rough calculation dividing the number of stars in the galaxy (200 billion) by the age of the galaxy (10 billion years) gives a mean rate of star formation of 20 stars per year, but most of these stars would have been formed in the early history of the galaxy. According to the calculations of Maarten Schmidt, formerly of Mount Wilson and Palomar Observatories, the present rate would be at least an order of magnitude less than the above, which gives an average star formation rate of about 1 star per year, giving a value of 1 for (R^*).

It was once thought that planetary systems were a rare accompaniment to stars; but the latest observations of dark companions of nearby stars and the sub-millimetre observations of dust discs around stars, together with the latest theories of planetary formation, imply that planetary systems are commonplace. This could imply that at least half the number of stars in our galaxy could have planetary companions giving a value 0.5 for (fp).

Considering our own planetary system the number of planets with environments favourable to life is at least one, possibly two if we include Mars. By extrapolation, we can adopt the figure 1 for (ne).

In general, if we accept the argument that, given sufficient time, life of some sort will develop when the environment is favourable we can take the value 1 for (fl).

It is very difficult to estimate the values for (fi) and (fc).

Shklovskii and Sagan give the probability of the evolution of intelligence on life-bearing planets in their book *Intelligent Life in the Universe*. They argue that although the evolution of intelligence is the result of the product of a large number of unlikely individual events the adaptive value of intelligence and manipulative ability is so great (see Kauffman, *The Origins of Order*) that if it is genetically feasible natural selection seems likely to bring it about. With the expectation that the earth is not unique as the abode of creatures with intelligence and manipulative ability but allowing for the fact that only one such species has developed in the history of the nine planets in the solar system they give a fraction of 0.1 for (fi).

They also argue that, with respect to geological time, it has taken only a very short time for our technical civilisation to arise, the earth is unlikely to be to be very extraordinary in this regards and give (fc) a value of 0.1.

These are very speculative figures, and will be adopted for the sake of argument.

The lifetime of advanced civilisations is again a matter of guesswork. Up to the present our own civilisation has lasted about 5,000 years but humans as we know them have been on earth for about 1,000,000 years. We can give the latter figure when consideration of religion is involved.

This gives the number of contemporary technical civilisations within our galaxy of,

$$N = 1.0 \times 0.5 \times 1.0 \times 1.0 \times 0.1 \times 0.1 \times 1,000\,000. = 5,000$$

Of course, if we discard the contemporary classification, which I suppose we should, if we are discussing the validity of religion, then we obtain a much higher upper limit. It is merely the number of stars in the galaxy (200 billion) replacing the mean rate of star formation in the above calculation, leaving out the lifetime of advanced civilisations.

This gives

$$200,000,000,000 \times 0.5 \times 1.0 \times 1.0 \times 0.1 \times 0.1 = 1,000,000,000$$

Either of these can be adopted as a highly speculative upper limit for the number of galactic extra terrestrial civilisations, although we can adopt a lower limit with absolute certainty as one. Since according to the Copernican Principle, that there is nothing special about our place in the universe, the assumption that there is, on average, at least one highly developed civilisation in every galaxy, seems eminently reasonable. The next question is: how many galaxies are there in the universe and how big are they?

Island Universes

In 1755, the philosopher Immanual Kant first proposed the idea of separate galaxies or nebulae, as they were originally designated. He suggested that each single nebula was an assemblage of stars of similar character and size as those that compose the whole Milky Way: the so-called 'Island Universe' theory of nebulae. This was at first accepted by William Herschel, the astronomer already mentioned with respect to star counts. Herschel had in fact observed such nebulae. As a matter of interest, he once stated that he had discovered 1,500 new universes. He later came to reject the idea that such nebulae were external to the Milky Way because their distribution seemed to favour regions of the sky far distant from the dense star region of the Milky Way, which represents the disc of our galaxy. He reasoned that if they were external to our galaxy then there was no reason for such a skewed distribution. He was, of course, unaware of the stellar extinction factor that is greater in the plane of the disc. Such extinction or absorption of light is caused by the vast clouds of gas and tiny solid particles (dust) that are found between the stars. By earthly standards, this space is very empty indeed but because there is so much space this gas and dust has a significant effect upon our optical viewing. In our observation of external galaxies, the absorption is so heavy in the region of the Milky Way that almost no external galaxies can be seen. More and more galaxies can be seen as one turns away from the Milky Way with a maximum at ninety degrees to the plane of the galactic disc where the extinction is at a minimum. This effect deceived Herschel in his observations of the 'nebulae'.

By 1908, some 15,000 nebulae had been catalogued and described but their nature was undetermined. It was not until the construction of the 60-inch and 120-inch telescopes at Mount Wilson that these nebulae were clearly established, from observations of the brightest variable stars within them, to be clearly extra-galactic. The famous astronomer Edwin Hubble accomplished this in 1924 when his observation of the light curves of variable stars in the nebulae M31, M33 and NGC6822 showed them to be entities known as Cepheids. Although Cepheids are in fact super giant stars they were so faint in Hubble's observations that they, and the systems they were in, had to be very remote from our own galaxy.

After Hubble had established the true nature of the 'nebulae', he made an extensive study of galaxies, including their distribution on the sky. He photographed 1,283 sample regions of the sky with the 60-inch telescope. These sample regions contained 44,000 galaxies. From this Hubble calculated that about 100,000,000 galaxies existed within the range of the 60-inch telescope. In addition, work had been going on to measure the radial velocities of the observed galaxies. That is the velocities either directly away or towards us. This is done by measurement of the galaxies 'redshift' or 'blueshift'.

The Redshift

If a galaxy is travelling away from us its light waves will impinge upon us less frequently than if it were travelling towards us. Without going into a detailed account of spectroscopy, the received frequency of its light can be found by examining the absorption and emission lines of a specific element, hydrogen, for instance, which in a static frame has such lines occurring at well-defined frequencies. If with respect to an external galaxy the frequency with which these lines appear is less than the static case then the galaxy is travelling away from us; and vice versa. Because light becomes redder at lower frequencies and bluer at higher frequencies a galaxy travelling away from us is said to have a 'redshift' and one travelling towards us a 'blueshift'. In his examination of the spectra of distant galaxies Hubble had found that they all had redshifts. In other words, all the distant galaxies were travelling away from us, which implied that the universe was in a state of expansion. In addition, he found that not only were the galaxies he had observed moving away, but that the speed of their recession was proportional to their distance from us. This does not imply that we are at the centre of the universe, since an observer on some distant galaxy, with respect to our own galaxy, would experience the same phenomena. By 1930 Hubble and Humason, observing a much larger sample, had also established that the more distant a galaxy the greater was its redshift or speed of recession. This is now known as Hubble's Law. At the present time, more and more galaxies and galactic objects have been observed with higher and higher redshifts. It has been calculated that the number of galaxies within the range of modern ground-based telescopes exceeds one billion. This does not take into account the many millions of galaxies that we cannot see because they are too small or too dim to observe at any distance.

Our galaxy is reasonably representative of a large number of galaxies in the universe. The advent of the latest space telescope, itself named Hubble after the famous astronomer, has increased the estimated number of observable galaxies by a factor of fifty. The observable universe thus contains a minimum of fifty billion galaxies, and that part of the universe that we cannot observe may contain many more, even an infinite number, if the universe itself is infinite in extent.

Many of the galaxies that we observe are very much larger than our own. For instance, the super-luminous Cd galaxy at the centre of the cluster of galaxies A2670 could be at least fifty times the size of the Milky Way. In general, though, our own spiral disc type galaxy with about 200 billion stars is of normal size.

The Displacement of Mankind and Religious Apologia

It seems that the extent of the universe, even that part of it that we observe, has totally displaced man from his central position so beloved of two main Western Religions, Judaism and Christianity Thus, their basic tenet is seriously undermined. Man, far from being the main and divine purpose of God's creation, has now been reduced to a bi-product of a bi-product, one life-form among many, arising from the residue of star formation. A process that has most probably been repeated billions of times over. How do the religious apologists deal with this situation?

Moslems can indeed point to a verse in the Koran

> 'The creation of the Heavens and of the Earth is indeed greater than the creation of mankind; yet, most of mankind know not.'
>
> (Surah 40, Surat Ghafir 57)

This appears to consider that the heavens and the earth are more complicated constructions than living beings, which is not true. Modern biologists consider the structure of living matter to be the most complicated known. The structure of the non-living matter of the universe is comparatively simple consisting mainly atoms of hydrogen and helium with a smattering of heavier elements. Life-forms are constructed from organic (carbon-rich) compounds. The proteins found in living organisms are built from one set of twenty standard amino acids and they include enzymes essential to development and reproduction. They also carry their genetic information in the nucleic acids RNA and DNA that use the genetic code specifying the amino-acid sequences of all the proteins each organism needs.

The idea that other living beings might exist on other planets within the universe was not even considered at the time of Muhammad, for the very good reason that the religion was initiated in a pre-Copernican age when such things did not enter the compass of known existence. In the light of later knowledge, it is indeed possible for Muslims to reinterpret this quotation as applying to the intelligent inhabitants of millions of other planets throughout the universe.

In Sahih Al-Bukhari (Vol 4, Chap 3, p282) Abu Qatadah mentions Allah's Statement 'And we have adorned the nearest heaven with lamps (Koran, Surah: 67 Surat Al-Mulk: 5) and says 'The creation of these stars is for three purposes, i.e. as decoration of the nearest heaven, as missiles to hit the devils [presumably meteors or 'Shooting Stars'.] And as signs to guide travellers. So if anybody tries to find a different interpretation he is mistaken and just wastes his efforts, and troubles himself with what is beyond his limited knowledge.'

This pre-empts the logical positivist philosophy of Wittgenstein and A J Ayer but they are not unreasonable conjectures in the pre-Copernican era before the invention of the telescope and the spectrograph. It must be admitted, that for us at least, the stars and planets do decorate the heavens, and they certainly are a guide to navigators. This seems more a result of man's ability to admire and make use of nature's artefacts, than a deliberate divine emplacement plan just for our benefit. It is of course possible for the religious apologist to claim them as the beneficial side effects of an overall divinity.

The late C S Lewis, the well-known Christian apologist, in his book, *Christian Reflections*, comments on the Russians reporting that they have not found God in outer space. The conclusions that can be drawn from this report he says are:

1   We have not yet gone far enough in space to find
     God.

2   God is locally confined to this planet.

3   The Russians did find God in space without knowing
     it because they lacked the requisite apparatus for
     detecting Him.

4   God is not an object in space or diffused through it.

5   God does not exist.

He claimed that the first two conclusions did not interest him. The sort of religion for which they would be a defence would be a religion for savages: the belief in a local deity who can be contained in a particular temple, island or grove.

Lewis should have been careful here. As a renowned classical scholar, he should have been aware that the ancient Greeks and Romans, who were far from being savages, had just such a religion, with the gods residing on Mount Olympus. The Jews also originally had a local god. First Jehovah, a god of the mountains and then the one true God, imageless and numinous, who dwelt in the Holy of Holies in the temple in Jerusalem with His footstool, the sacred Ark of the Covenant containing the tablets of the Decalogue. In Lewis's own religion, Christianity Jesus Christ is local not only to this planet but to a rather small area of ancient Palestine. To a hypothetical advanced space traveller the three Western Religions would indeed be 'local' in the sense that they are confined to one small planet of a rather insignificant star in a somewhat insignificant galaxy.

Such local beliefs, so easily dismissed as the beliefs of savages, had great relevance to the ancients because this planet earth assumed the guise of the whole universe, with mankind at its epicentre. The Russians were in fact indicating that the discovery of the true vastness of the universe had shown the insignificance of mankind and his parochial beliefs. They did not really expect to find God lurking somewhere in space.

The third conclusion is declared invalid since God is related to the universe in the same way that an author is related to his manuscript. He can no more be found by examining space-time than Shakespeare can be found by examining his plays. This is a reasonable attitude to take but it does not give credence to the three main Western Religions that have God continually interfering in the doings of humanity. After all, one does not find Shakespeare entering into *Romeo and Juliet* to ensure a happy ending. To meet this objection Lewis readjusts his analogy and considers Dante's *Divine Comedy* where Dante is both a character in the story and also its author. However, this appears to repudiate the idea of free will, which forms an essential part of penitence and redemption.

Lewis continues, using special pleading to question the Copernican Principle. Echoing the *Astronomical Discourses* of Thomas Chalmers, published in 1817, Lewis speculates that other intelligent life forms might not, like us, need redemption. This puts us under special consideration and questions the universality of physics and hence biology. He also postulates the far-fetched idea of preaching Christianity to beings inhabiting other worlds. There are possibly billions of other worlds, most of them billions of light years away from us. We could not even communicate, never mind proselytise. Finally, despairing of all reasoned logical argument, he uses the last resort of the religious apologist: 'We will have to cross that bridge when we come to it.'

Professor William Whewell, philosopher, scientist, Master of Trinity College Cambridge, used similar arguments in 1853. 'There is no proof that other solar systems exist. The stars may be of different construction than the sun. Other stars are binary and so cannot have planetary systems.' In 1853, the science of spectroscopy was in its infancy and observational equipment was relatively primitive. His arguments therefore appeared more convincing than they do today. To reiterate such arguments when observations have confirmed the universality of physical laws seems reactionary at best. Lewis, although an expert on mediaeval literature, did not have enough knowledge of cosmology to inform his arguments.

The fourth conclusion, 'God is not an object in space or diffused through it', Lewis relates to morality and ethics. He also examines the status of objective values for instance mathematics. Again, this is a reasonable enough argument but such an argument does not necessarily confer validity upon the Western Religions. These ideas are discussed again later in this book when we look at mysticism and science.

The fifth conclusion that, God does not exist, is also an intellectually respectable one, although not quite so easy to justify, as it seems at first glance. Of course, as a convinced (Christian) theist convert from atheism, Lewis does not adhere to it but holds respect for those who do so out of intellectual conviction.

In his book, *We Have Reason to Believe*, the Jewish apologist Rabbi Louis Jacobs deals with 'Scientific Difficulties'. He claims that present-day religious thinkers consider the Bible not as a scientific-text book but as a work of guidance and inspiration in the realm of religion and morals. Therefore, we must not expect its opinions on scientific matters to be 'up to date'. If eternal truth is to be revealed to man, it can only be transmitted in the thought patterns of the age in which the revelation takes place. This is a fair enough comment but the problem underlying the whole essence of the Torah and other religious works remains. This lies in the pre-Copernican belief that man is the essential purpose of creation and that the universe consists only of his earthly domain together with heaven and hell, also constructed for the redemption or damnation of mankind as their main purpose.

In his book, *Alone in the Universe*, the Rev Dr David Wilkinson presents an overall discussion of the problem and attempts to reconcile the results of modern cosmology with religion, particularly his own religion, Christianity. It is hardly an impartial tract, which is understandable since the Rev Wilkinson is a Methodist chaplain in addition to having a PhD in Theoretical

Astrophysics. After an examination of the effects of science fiction, cult beliefs and UFO claimants upon modern society, he gets down to the serious consideration of the post-Copernican universe. He claims that our understanding of the biological origin of life and the development of intelligence seems to point to the high probability that we are alone in the universe. He bases these claims upon calculations by Sir Fred Hoyle and Chandra Wickramasinghe that the probability of the spontaneous generation of a bacterium is so unlikely that in fact we should not exist, the likelihood of such an event, being comparable to the chances of a wind sweeping through a junkyard, and assembling a Boeing 747 from the junk. The implicit assumption is that as we do exist, we must have been specially created through evolution by divine favour and therefore, although modified by the discoveries of modern science, we are the epitome of creation after all and Christianity a religion of validity. A happy and justifiable conclusion! Alternatively, it seems rather odd, to say the least, that this vast, possibly infinite universe has been created for the benefit of the inhabitants of a small insignificant planet. To be fair to Wilkinson, he does mention Stuart Kauffman, whose ideas and experimental work on the phenomena of self-organisation can be read in his books *At Home in the Universe* and *The Origins of Order*, the first book being a popular exposition of the second, which is highly technical.

Kauffman deals with the probability argument of Hoyle and Wickramasinghe 'that we should not exist', as follows:

'Since you are reading this book, and I am writing it, something must be wrong with the argument. The problem, I believe, is that Hoyle, Wickramasinghe, and many others have failed to appreciate the power of self-organisation. It is not necessary that a specific set of 2000 enzymes be assembled, one by one, to carry out a specific set of reactions. As we shall see, there are compelling reasons to believe that whenever a collection of chemicals contains enough different kinds of molecules, a metabolism will crystallise from the broth. If this argument is correct, metabolic networks need not be built one component at a time; they can spring full-grown from a primordial soup. Order for free, I call it. If I am right, the motto of life is not We the improbable, but We the expected.'

Life in the Universe

Hoyle and Wickramasinghe use their calculations to argue for panspermia, the seeding of the universe with elementary bacteria, controlled by some mysterious extra-galactic super-intelligence. Kauffman's ideas are literally more down-to-earth and I think more convincing. Confirmation of the independent formation of bacterial life on Mars, recently discovered in a meteorite of Martian origin, would certainly give great impetus to his theory of self-organisation and the ubiquity of life throughout the universe. Wilkinson stresses that this is a minority view among biologists, but an even smaller minority of biologists accept divine special creation on this planet alone, or universal panspermia.

Wilkinson also raises Enrico Fermi's argument. Fermi advances the scientific view that, were intelligent aliens in existence, they should have found us by now. His basic argument claims that as the earth is much younger than the galaxy, then civilisations would have arisen on other planets within the galaxy many millions or even billions of years ago. If this were the case then at least some of them would have embarked on space colonisation. This would be done most efficiently by the construction of artificial brains contained in machines that would be self-reproducing, using materials gathered from suitable planets. Such machines are called Von Neumann machines, after the scientist who established their theoretical possibility. If this were the case then it is a reasonable assumption that the corresponding rocket technology would be equally advanced. With an interstellar speed of about ten per cent of the speed of light and an exponential increase in the number of machines with time, it is calculated that the whole galaxy could be colonised within 300,000,000 years. As the galaxy is approximately fifteen to twenty billion years old, then the machines should be here by now. As there is no compelling evidence that any aliens have visited earth, we must be alone in the galaxy.

There are various counter-arguments to this. For example, the economics of Von Neumann machine colonisation would mean excessive expenditure for an unknown and uncertain return. Such expenditure could well be prohibitive. Again, the technical problems of constructing Von Neumann machines to function for hundreds of millions of years could well be insurmountable, even if such expenditure could be found. In addition, the projected exponential expansion rate of the construction of the Von Neumann machines could be limited by physical factors within the galaxy. Even if Fermi is correct in his postulation, this still does not rule out civilisations arising on the billions of other galaxies in the universe, or even within the distant regions of our own galaxy. The nearest reasonably sized galaxy, the Andromeda spiral galaxy, is about 2,000,000 light years away. This is about twenty times further than the diameter of our own galaxy. It seems highly unlikely that any technical civilisation would bridge intergalactic distances, especially when most other galaxies are billions rather than millions of light years distant.

A Possible REAL UFO

As a matter of interest with respect to Fermi's argument, a paper submitted to *The Observatory* (the journal of the Royal Astronomical Society) in 1991 by Duncan Steel, described a ten-metre object, designated 1991VG, on a heliocentric orbit that made its closest approach to earth in December 1991. Jim Scotti discovered it with the Spacewatch telescope at Kitt Peak on 6th November. Its very earth-like orbit and rapid brightness fluctuations argued for it being an artificial body rather than an asteroid. None of the handful of man-made rocket bodies left in heliocentric orbits during the space age had purely gravitational orbits returning to earth at that time. In addition, the close distance observed may be interpreted as a controlled rather than a random encounter with earth. It could therefore be argued that 1991VG is a candidate for an alien probe observed in the vicinity of our planet.

The details are given as follows: the 0.91-m Spacewatch telescope of the University of Arizona at Kitt Peak commenced operation in 1989, since when it has been used to detect asteroids of an unprecedented small size in the earth's vicinity. In November 1991 observer Jim Scotti discovered a body initially described as being a fast moving asteroidal object. However, observations by Richard West and Oliver Hainaut from ESO close to the time of nearest approach indicated a non-asteroidal nature of the object, with strong rapid brightness variations, which can be interpreted as transient specular reflections from the surfaces of a rotating spacecraft. The paper then investigates the different probabilities for the nature of this object. It seems that the probability that it is a returning man-made rocket or spacecraft is extremely low. Similarly for the probability of it being a natural asteroid. Hence the paper concludes that the observations provide *prima facie* evidence that 1991VG is a candidate alien artefact. The alternative explanations, that it was a peculiar asteroid or a man-made body, are both estimated to be unlikely, but require further investigation. If in fact it is a returned man-made rocket body it was very much a fluke that it was observed, and the normal process of science then requires that we consider the possibility of some other origin. The next near-passage of 1991VG is calculated to be in 2041, by which time it is hoped that our instrumentation will be good enough to determine its true origin.

A Historical Analogy

The idea that intelligent life cannot exist elsewhere in the universe bears an interesting comparison with the argument that men could not exist in the antipodes (the opposite side of the earth). This argument was prevalent in the sixth century. A proponent of this view was the eminent Christian authority Saint Augustine. He stated that 'Scripture speaks of no such descendants of Adam'. He insists that men could not be allowed by God to live there since they would be unable to see Christ at his second coming. He referred to both the nineteenth psalm and its confirmation in the Epistle to the Romans, where regarding the preachers of the gospel, Saint Paul states that 'Verily their sound went into all the earth, and their words unto the ends of the world'. In other words since these preachers did not go to the antipodes, the antipodes must be uninhabited.

Further Apologetics

In the final section of his book, the Rev Wilkinson deals with the 'truth' of Christianity in a rather strange way. He does not explicitly rule out the existence of aliens on other worlds although he finds the possibility extremely unlikely. Nevertheless, just in case there are such aliens, how is the Christian message to reach them from earth where the momentous event of Christ's birth, life, death and resurrection took place? Wilkinson admits that the vast distances involved would rule out any missionary projects but goes on to reiterate a remarkable claim made by our old friend Thomas Chalmers in 1817, that 'a person can be saved through Christ without ever having heard of Christ'. He gives the example of Abraham who, he claims, was saved by looking forward to Christ rather than looking back on Him. I find no evidence of this in my own study of Genesis but as I am not a professional Biblical scholar, I defer to the Reverend Wilkinson. But this does raise the question of the relevance of missionaries. Why bother to go to all the trouble and danger of sending missionaries to convert the heathen when their salvation can be assured without their ever having heard of Christ? This seems to me 'special pleading' indeed.

There are really only three choices for the serious scholar.

1 Reconcile religion with modern science.

2 Reject modern science.

3 Reject religion.

Most Christian apologists today accept the first option. As we have seen, this is very difficult because unlike plain Deism, it requires the denial of the Copernican Principle. It involves explaining the incarnation and the redemption and for this we needs must be special. No convincing reconciliation has yet been made. All attempts end up, one way or another, in terms of crossing bridges when we come to them. The difficulties for the orthodox Jewish apologist are almost as bad. He does not have the incarnation to explain but he does have the Messianic tradition and chosen exclusivity with which to deal.

The non-orthodox progressive Jew who is sceptical of Jewish exclusivity and who secularises the Messianic tradition to a 'Messianic Age' of peace and plenty, can retreat into Deism but must still explain the theistic notion of good and evil.

The Islamic apologist still has to explain the final judgement and the existence of heaven and hell. It is easier for the Islamic mystic since he can claim that the transcendence of God overrides any requirement or necessity for such explanation and that the references to judgement day, etc., are not to be taken literally but figuratively in a mystical sense. We have seen that the Eastern religions in general do not have these anthropomorphic difficulties.

Religious fundamentalists including Christian creationists take the second choice, rejecting modern science. Many of them follow the teachings of Gosse who in 1857, in a work entitled *Omphalos,* pronounced that all evidence of geological changes and long epochs in strata were appearances only and nothing more. God created these appearances instantaneously 6,000 years ago. Among them were glacial furrows, piles of lava from extinct volcanoes and fossils of every sort all over the earth. The preface to the work ends with a prayer that science can thus be reconciled to the Holy Scriptures.

In fact, radioactive dating, unknown to Gosse at the time, can show that various structures on the earth have vastly different ages. If this is not accepted, then taking such an argument to its logical conclusion, there is nothing to deny that the universe, including ourselves with all our memories, together with the Holy Scriptures, was created yesterday or two milliseconds ago!

Free Will

The third option, 'Reject religion', is that taken by atheistic or agnostic scientists such as Richard Dawkins and Stephen Hawking. Some scientists, Dr Dean E Wooldridge for example, go to the extreme of physical materialism and determinism, denying not only religion but also free will. Man is considered as a purely mechanical artifice.

Free will is itself a subject of great philosophical dispute. D J O'Connor in his book *Free Will* comes to the conclusion that the whole idea is inconclusive. This is rather unsatisfactory since it seems to me that without free will nothing could be inconclusive. The fact that free will governs thoughts as well as actions would appear to make the debate about free will itself an example of free will. We can invalidate any deterministic prediction made for us by simply refusing to conform. The example O'Conner gives, of the evolutionary advantage of determinism for a creature to be able to read the evidence correctly to avoid predators, can be turned on its head. Firstly, creatures do not always read the evidence correctly, otherwise there would be no predators left. Secondly, the development of free will must confer a considerable advantage to both the hunter and the hunted. Presumably, insects for example, do not act under free will but have automatic responses to events affecting them. As we proceed up the scale of animal intelligence, the effect of free thought and action becomes more apparent. It appears that free will is a necessary accompaniment of intelligence. Furthermore, the inconclusiveness of modern quantum theory is a blow to the scientific determinism of the last century. An attempt to rescue it leads to ideas such as the 'Many Worlds Theory', which will be discussed more fully in Chapter Five.

Summary

In this chapter, the vastness of the universe is examined. Commencing with the earth and the solar system, continuing with the extent of our galaxy, and concluding with the fifty billion galaxies made visible in the observed universe by the Hubble space telescope.

Both the history and methods of calculating the distance of the stars and the galaxies are described (without mathematical formulae). The probability of life and advanced civilisations within the galaxy, and hence the whole universe is discussed, particularly with reference to the method first given by Frank Drake.

It is the displacement of mankind from the central role in our universe that appears to have undermined many of the basic tenets of the three Western Religions. In respect of this, the views of C S Lewis are presented, as well as those of Rabbi Louis Jacobs and the Rev Davis Wilkinson. Various relevant quotations from the Bible and the Koran are also discussed.

The problem of the origin of life in the universe is given, with reference to the theories of Hoyle and Wickramasinghe, and the counter-theory of self-organisation argued by Stuart Kauffman.

Fermi's 'Why aren't they here?' argument, against the existence of extra-terrestrials, is presented, together with the observations in 1991 by Scotti, West and Hainaut, of what might possibly be an artificially constructed extra-terrestrial object.

The final section introduces the problem of 'free will', and argues that it seems to be a necessary accompaniment to intelligence in living systems.

Next, we look at some of the problems for religion raised by scientific history and the possible prospects in store for our universe.

CHAPTER THREE

Time

WHERE DOES IT ALL GO TO?

In this chapter we will examine the discoveries of modern cosmology with respect to time and see how these compare to traditional religious concepts. Time, as it is generally understood here, is scientifically referred to as 'proper time' (see Chapter Four), in contrast to 'subjective time' experienced psychologically by a particular individual at some particular reference point.

There has been great dispute among religious authorities as to the time God took to create the universe. Two accounts of the creation are given in Genesis. The first extends the operation through six days with much explicit detail given for each day. The second speaks of 'the day' in which the Lord God made the earth and the heavens. This resulted in the doctrine that in some mysterious way God created the universe in six days and yet at the same time brought it all into existence in an instant; an idea promoted by both St Athanasius and St Augustine.

St Thomas Aquinas eased the incompatibility of the two accounts by teaching that God created the substance of things instantaneously but then took six days to create the universe from this substance, much as an artist mixes his paints before painting a picture.

The Age of the Universe

The pre-Copernican values of the extent of time in the world are, from the modern point of view, very limited. For example, the age of the universe was calculated by a Dr John Lightfoot, Vice Chancellor of the University of Cambridge who was one of the most eminent Hebrew scholars of the age. As a result of his most profound and exhaustive study of the Scriptures, he declared that 'Heaven and earth, centre and circumference were created altogether, in the same instant, and that man was created by the Trinity on October 23rd 4004BC at nine o'clock in the morning'. The fact that this may well have coincided with the start of the Cambridge autumn term would obviously be most convenient.

Calvin opposed the idea of an instantaneous creation, stressing the creation in six days. He also stated that biblical chronology shows the world to be not quite six thousand years old. Peter Martyr, one of the Westminster Divines, declared, 'So important is it to comprehend the work of creation that the Church takes this as its starting point. Were this article taken away there would be no original sin, the promise of Christ would become void, and all the vital force of our religion would be destroyed.'

In the seventeenth century no less a person than the great Sir Isaac Newton gives a prime example of special pleading. He believed in the literal truth of the creation story that God created the universe in six days. However, like al-Biruni, he claimed that nowhere in the Scriptures does it say that all six days were of equal length. During the first two days, for instance, there was no earth and therefore no twenty-four-hour day based upon planetary rotation. The length of either of these could therefore have been anything God wished.

At present, we tend naturally to look at time on scales within an order or two of our own average lifetime (about 70 to 7,000 years). For instance, the Jews imagine that they have a very old religion, almost five thousand years from the days of Abraham. Certainly in the pre-Copernican era that was very old indeed, in fact almost

Time	Event
Zero	God created Earth, Heaven and all that is therein in six days
1,000 years	The flood
1,500 years	Abraham
2,800 years	Exodus
3,000 years	The conquest of the land of Canaan
3,400 years	The Babylonian captivity
3,480 years	The return to Jerusalem
3,700 years	The Greek conquests
3,950 years	The Roman conquests
4,000 years	The life and death of Jesus of Nazareth
4,300 years	Rome becomes Christian under the Emperor Constantine
4,500 years	The fall of the Western Empire and the onset of the dark ages
5,200 years	The establishment of Papal authority and the Renaissance
5,450 years	The fall of Eastern Empire to the Turks
5,500 years	The Reformation
6,000 years	The present day

TABLE ONE: THE CHRISTIAN/JUDIAC TIMESCALE OF CREATION

Proper Time   Event

Proper Time	Event
Zero	Big Bang
1 second	Annihilation of electron-positron pairs
1 minute	Formation of hydrogen and helium atoms
10,000 years	Universe becomes Matter dominated
300,000 years	Universe becomes transparent
3-4 billion years	Galaxy formation and clustering begins
4-5 billion years	First primeval stars form in the galaxies
10 billion years	Second generation stars form
15.3 billion years	Formation of our solar system with protosolar nebula
15.4 billion years	Planets form and rock solidifies
16.1 billion years	The first terrestrial rocks form
17 billion years	Microscopic life forms
19.5 billion years	First land plants
19.6 billion years	First fish
19.8 billion years	Mountains, Conifers and reptiles
19.9 billion years	Dinosaurs
19.95 billion years	First Mammals
20 billion years	Homo sapiens

TABLE TWO: THE SCIENTIFIC TIMEASCALE OF THE UNIVERSE

as old as the implicit age of the universe. In modern scientific terms, the age of the universe is estimated using the distance-redshift relation together with an estimate of the universal deceleration parameter. This is done by careful and diligent observation of various galactic markers, all of which have a wide margin of error (for a full technical account see Weinberg's *Gravitation and Cosmology*). This gives the age of the universe as between ten and twenty billion years.

Accurate geological observations, using radioactive dating, show the age of the earth itself to be about four billion years. By comparison, the term of Judaism is not even a dot on time's horizon.

We can easily manipulate large numbers in mathematics but we have a major psychological problem attempting to comprehend them physically. We find it impossible to conceptualise such vast aeons of time or the immensity of distances within the universe. For instance, we tend to think of distances in terms of an order or two of the distance that a man could comfortably travel by foot in a day, from 20 miles to about 2,000 miles. When it comes to billions and billions of light years, our imagination fails us and we have to rely on the mathematics; whereas in pre-Copernican times both distance and time remained within our comprehension. The vast age of the universe sets certain problems for the pre-Copernican religions. In the early eras of the earth's existence, the only life-forms shown in the geological records are the very simplest single-celled organisms without even nuclei, known as prokaryotic cells. It took another three billion years before life-forms that are more complex evolved. The wide diversity of these complex life-forms, brought about by evolution and natural selection appears, by fortuitous accident within the last million years or so, to have culminated in mankind.

At what stage in the evolutionary story did his soul develop? Do all life-forms possess some form of soul or élan vital? Most biologists now would emphatically deny the existence of any such thing, although there is certainly a mystery with respect to the development of consciousness and identity.

A further problem arises when we consider the prospect of 'Judgement Day'. Such a time limit does not exist in modern cosmology. The consensus of astronomers measures time from the 'Big Bang' origin of the universe: the general idea being that if the universe is expanding at some estimated rate, then in theory, at some considerable time in the past (ten to twenty billion years), the distance between any two points in the universe must have been arbitrarily close and the density of matter must have been infinite. The age of the universe is measured from this time. What happened before this, if there was a 'before this', is pure speculation. This expansion of the universe is considered the expansion of space itself, not the clusters of galaxies rushing away from each other through space. Applying the radioactive technique to uranium and using detailed models of galactic evolution, we infer the age of the galaxy to be about ten billion years. The age of a star can be inferred from its mass since the total supply of hydrogen in the core specifies its luminosity for a specific chemical composition. Using spectroscopy to determine the chemical composition with a model of stellar evolution, the oldest stars in the galaxy give an approximate age of twelve billion years. The remarkable convergence of these three time-scales is regarded as evidence favouring a finite age for the universe. If this is indeed the case then the temperature of the universe at the time of the 'Big Bang' must have been extreme. Calculations made by Robert Dicke and his group from Princeton University showed that the 'Big Bang' provided a very likely environment for the production of helium, which today constitutes about thirty per cent of the mass of the universe. They also calculated that the cooling of the universe from the time of the 'Big Bang' would give a present day universal background temperature less than forty degrees Kelvin and would be detectable in the microwave background (0 degrees Kelvin equals -273 degrees Celsius, the temperature at which all atomic motion ceases, known as absolute zero).

The Cosmic Microwave Background

In 1965, the radio astronomers Arno Penzias and Robert Wilson made a series of measurements with a radio telescope developed by Bell Laboratories in Holmdel, New Jersey. They found excess radio noise at a wavelength of 735mm that appeared to be independent of direction in the sky. After calibrating the telescope and hence eliminating the possibility of any terrestrial origin of the noise, they concluded that the radiation was uniform in all directions. It did not differ intensity in the direction of the Milky Way or of any specific astronomical bodies and hence could not be of galactic origin.

This radiation was equivalent to a universal background temperature of 3.5 degrees Kelvin (K). The intensity of the background radiation has since been measured at many wavelengths and has been found to give a spectrum in keeping with the time when matter and radiation were in equilibrium at a temperature of about 3,000 degrees K. It has also been found to possess a very high degree of uniformity (any smoothness discrepancy being less than 1 part in 10,000). This confirms that it is a genuine measurement of the cosmic background temperature. Any other source would produce distortion effects. This is regarded as a very strong confirmation of the 'Big Bang'.

A further independent confirmation is given by the abundance and distribution of helium in the galaxy. The distribution seems to be even and the abundance of one helium atom for every ten hydrogen atoms gives far more helium than could be provided by its production in stars through hydrogen burning (fusion). Furthermore, helium has been found in the same abundance in many other galaxies. The high temperatures and densities predicted for the early moments of the 'Big Bang' are very conducive to the production of hydrogen and helium, these being the lightest elements.

The Death of the Steady State Theory and Olber's Paradox

These three independent factors, the converging time-scales, the helium abundance and above all the cosmic microwave background, all lead to the conclusion that our universe originated in the 'Big Bang' between ten and twenty billion years ago. There are still a few dissident voices, namely Fred Hoyle, Gold, Bondi and Narlikar, but they postulate a 'Steady State' theory that advocates the eternal existence of the universe without beginning or end and a continual creation of matter (hydrogen). The present observational evidence presented above provides strong reasons for discounting such a theory.

Another reason for discounting the 'steady state' theory is the consideration of what is known as 'Olbers' paradox'. Heinrich Olbers was a German amateur astronomer and mathematician. In 1823, he raised the problem of a paradox that now bears his name, although the Swiss astronomer J L de Cheseaux first noticed it. The paradox goes as follows.

If the universe is static and infinite in time and space, with an infinite number of stars, then since (a) the brightness of stars decreases with the square of the distance from us and, (b) the number of stars increases with the square of the distance, these two factors would cause the night sky to be infinitely bright. A more refined calculation takes into account the fact that the nearby stars block out the light from the more distant ones but this still leaves the night sky as bright as the surface of the sun. Since this obviously does not hold, why is the sky dark at night?

One answer would be that there are only a finite number of stars in the universe. If this were the case, then a static universe would long ago have collapsed into itself by gravitational attraction. This implies that the universe is not static and can therefore only be expanding. Another answer could be that the universe has existed for a finite period. Since the speed of light is finite, the observable universe would have a radius equal to the distance that light could travel within the period of its existence. Thus, only those stars within such a radius would be observed.

If we combine the idea of an expanding universe leading to a redshift diminution of starlight intensity with a finite time of existence, we are led directly to the 'Big Bang'. The 'Steady State' theory, with galaxies being continually created throughout infinite time, would not resolve Olber's paradox completely even with expansion taken into account.

In addition, there is evidence that the universe was different in the past. This evidence takes the form, firstly of radio telescope observations. When we look at distant objects in the universe, we are in fact looking backwards in time because of the finite speed of light. The more distant the object as measured by the redshift, the further back in time we see it. If the 'Steady State' theory were true then the past would look exactly like the present. As far as these radio observations are concerned this is not so. By counting radio sources at different distances, it seems that the universe was much more congested with such sources in the past (Revised 3rd *Cambridge Catalogue of Northern Hemisphere Sources*). Secondly, optical observations of galaxies have thrown up a further discrepancy. In 1978 two astronomers, Butcher and Oemler, observing distant galaxies, found that in the past a higher percentage of galaxies were more energetic. This was most probably the result of more star formation within them. This has since been confirmed by further observations by Kron (1980), Shanks et al (1983), Ellis and Allen (1983) and my own observations (1983). In other words, the universe is evolving. Such evolution would not be viable in a 'Steady State' universe. If such a theory were true, it would raise even more problems for the pre-Copernican religions.

The Problem of the Hidden Matter and the Apocalypse

One of the main unsolved problems of today's universe is concerned with the quantity of matter it contains. Basically, if there is enough to bring an end to the expansion and cause the universe eventually to collapse, then the universe is designated closed and will end in a fireball similar in many ways to its beginning. Frank Tippler, among others, has estimated it, that if this is the case, the time from now to the final moment would be at least 100 billion years (see *The Physics of Immortality*, Appendix B, by Frank Tippler for a detailed calculation). This seems to some religious apologists to be an ideal solution to the idea of a 'Judgement Day'. By special pleading, we could have a day of judgement for the whole universe. Nevertheless, this is not the day of judgement specified by the pre-Copernican religions. Their judgement day involves the raising of the dead on earth, and for Christians, the second coming of Christ.

In fact, according to the New Testament this should have occurred within the lifetimes of those contemporary to Jesus (St Mark 14: 30). The fact that it did not has given rise to various sophistries on the part of the religious authorities. This apocalyptic aspect of Christianity was responsible for the church's antipathy to science. If the second coming of Christ was immanent, then good Christians should pay heed to their faith and not waste their time investigating nature.

('For the Jews require a sign, and the Greeks seek after wisdom:

But we preach Christ crucified, unto the Jews a stumbling block, and unto the Greeks foolishness').

Corinthians 22: 23

If there is not enough matter within the universe to halt its expansion then it will expand forever and must therefore be designated 'open'. In this case, it will eventually suffer what is known as the heat death, an inexorable consequence of the Second Law of Thermodynamics.

Thermodynamics and the Heat Death

The science of thermodynamics began with the use of steam engines. The engineer, Sadi Carnot, first analysed the problem of how to build the most efficient steam engine. In fact, he deduced the Second Law before the First Law was established. The laws of thermodynamics are:

> **The Zeroth Law**: If two systems have the same heat energy as a third system, then their heat energies must be equal.

> **The First Law**: The total energy of a system is equal to the work done on the system plus the heat absorbed by the system.

> **The Second Law**: In any closed system the amount of disorder (entropy) in the system will always increase with time.

A simple example of the second law would be that of pouring hot water onto blocks of ice. Melting would destroy the ordered structure of the ice, increasing the total disorder of the system, provided nothing external to the system is introduced, like a refrigerator for example. In other words, the system must be 'closed'. In no way would it be possible, in this case, for some of the hot water to turn to ice while the remainder was made even hotter. Heat can only flow from a hot substance to a cold substance and never the reverse, without outside interference.

From the scientific point of view, there could not be a better example of a closed system than the complete universe. If the universe is to continue to expand forever, then in compliance with the second law it will tend to a state of maximum disorder when all temperature differences and hence all heat flow are extinguished leaving a totally inactive and dead universe. This is what is meant by the 'heat death'. The most notable manifestation of this approaching quiescence is the continuous stellar radiation into space.

At the present moment the general balance of observational evidence favours this second option (see *Is the Universe Open or Closed?* by Peter Coles and George F R Ellis). Considering the fate of planet earth and its inhabitants, there are at least two ways in which the existence of our planet could end by external forces. It could be destroyed by the impact of a giant asteroid or comet similar to the impact of the comet Shumaker, on planet Jupiter. If such a comet had hit earth, it would almost certainly have destroyed the planet, together with all its varied life-forms. If this doesn't happen, in about four or five billion years, when our sun has used up much of its nuclear energy, it will expand into a red giant star and its radius will reach almost to the planet Mars. The earth will then be absorbed into the sun and slowly start to vaporise. Finally, its orbit slowed by the sun's gasses, it will plunge into the sun's fiery interior to reach its end.

(A simplified account of the technical aspect of this scenario can be found in Abell's *Exploration of the Universe*, Chapter Thirty-one).

The Fate of Planet Earth and the Book of Revelation

What of the future of humanity? We could meet our end before the demise of planet earth in various ways.

For example, a drastic change in the atmosphere or climate could seal our fate. The greenhouse effect could make the earth uninhabitable for oxygen-breathing creatures like ourselves. Other alternatives are: a deadly plague that spares no one, a thermonuclear conflict, or possibly destruction by an alien invasion. None of these last three possibilities seems very likely. Even the worst plagues find some resistance and although an atomic war could have the most dreadful consequences, it is unlikely that it would kill off everybody. An alien invasion, although dear to the hearts of UFO spotters, could only be launched from within our own galaxy, and as we have seen in the previous chapter the probability of such an event is extremely low. Humanity is more likely to be eradicated by an asteroidal collision or climatic catastrophe or even the eruption of a super-volcanic explosion than plague or war.

Where in all this universal history can the pre-Copernican religions place their day of judgement? According to St John, writing from his exile in Patmos: 'There will appear to our Earthly senses one like unto the son of man with streaming white hair and eyes as a flame of fire to raise the dead from their Earthly abode whence they shall be judged together with the living.' From the vantage point of modern cosmology, this does not take into account the millions of planets where life may have just started to form. Are all their prospects to be cut short just because of us? It is but a relic of some pre-Copernican prophetic myth, brilliantly described in the Book of Revelation, but inadequate in the light of modern science. Looked at from the religious point of view, however, it is not necessarily written as a prophecy, but is meant to warn against spiritual indifference, to elicit courage under persecution and to signify the ultimate victory of Christ. Nevertheless, many Biblical interpreters do look upon it as a prophecy, depicting events that are to take place at the end of the age. Many people, guided by orthodox priests, rabbis and mullahs, believe it implicitly. All the scientific knowledge gained since the time of Galileo appears not to have touched them. In some respects, this even applies to the Vatican that has several cosmologists among the Jesuit community, and holds conferences on modern cosmology. This cannot be due to ignorance but involves special pleading combined with a curious form of double belief.

The special pleading can involve aspects of modern cosmology. For instance, the 'Big Bang' has been taken by the Vatican to imply a divine creation, which of course it could well do. Then the double belief takes over, suggesting that in some mysterious way this validates the pre-Copernican Bible in its entirety. In 1952 Pope Pius

XII gave a talk to the Pontifical Academy in which he stated that the 'Big Bang' cosmology affirmed the notion of a transcendental Creator and is thus in harmony with Christian dogma. Similar attitudes pervade traditional aspects of the Jewish and Moslem religions. In some strange and unexplainable manner, it is possible to believe all of the modern scientific discoveries and still maintain the literal truth of the Torah and Koran.

Of course, the red queen in Alice could believe six impossible things before breakfast.

The Evolution of Man

A fascinating point of view, from which to mark the passage of time through the universe, is to examine the progress of evolution on our own planet. Man has existed as a separate creature for less than two million years. That is less than one thousandth of the time that life has existed on earth, which itself still has about five billion years to go. Barring accidents, what sort of creatures will we become over such a vast time span?

There is a book called *Man after Man* by Dougal Dixon. It concerns the anthropology of the future. Evolution has so far shaped man together with the world's fauna and flora, but according to Dixon, with the progress of modern technology, the future shapes of all life-forms will be determined, not by the slow and uncertain march of natural selection but by the deliberate machinations of mankind. Genetic engineering of human beings would entail removing a reproductive cell from a human, altering a known gene in a predetermined way and replacing the cell so that it grows to a full-term foetus with the required characteristics. This of course would require a much more advanced technique of genetic manipulation than we possess at present, but it appears inevitable that such techniques will eventually be acquired.

Starting his prognostications only 200 years in the future, Dixon postulates the 'aquamorph':

'Fish-like and frog-like the aquamorph is genetically adapted to live within a totally marine environment. Each physical feature – the streamlined body with the smooth skin and the insulating blubber layer, the gills on the chest, the paddles on the legs – was grown by the embryo. But this embryo was the result of manipulation of the sperm and egg cells. The chromosomal make-up was adjusted, creating genes that would produce features such as skin with a low drag factor, and the whole organism was allowed to grow to its designed form.'

This creature is essentially human. The book goes on to investigate the conquest of space within our galaxy, envisaging the design of the 'vacumorph' that can work in the free-fall and airless void of space orbit. As time progresses, many different species of humankind are developed, which at times war with each other and at other times complement each other. The book takes us forward 5,000,000 years, only a tenth of the time that our world has to run, but the picture presented is so strange and alien that memory of any of our present religions would have long ago faded out. What is disturbing about this book is the prognostication that the progress of science and technology is erratic and intermittent. There is none of the optimism of such people as Freeman Dyson or Frank Tippler, who consider that scientific progress is unstoppable, that although it may encounter setbacks it will finally embrace the universe to the advantage of all life. On the contrary, *Man after Man* shows a combination of technology with primitive savagery that condemns life to continual struggle and regression.

None of this speculation holds much hope for our present pre-Copernican religions. As far as our universe is concerned, it seems that we are contained, figuratively speaking, in a box with respect to both space and time: a box that has shrunk from the all-embracing vastness of the pre Copernican world to the present dot on the universal horizon. What then is the scientific basis, if any, for the belief in God and a divine origin of the universe?

Summary

This chapter discusses time with respect to modern cosmology and compares it with time as seen from the point of view of the pre-Copernican religions. The religious view vastly underestimates the time that the universe has existed, presenting problems, which has led to special pleading by religious authorities. The modern estimate, giving the age of the universe as fifteen to twenty billion years from the 'Big Bang' is discussed in detail. The problem of conceptualising such vast figures in time and space is also mentioned. The laws of thermodynamics are given, with especial reference to the second law, and the projected heat death of the universe. There is a problem reconciling this with such religious concepts as 'The Resurrection' and 'Judgement Day'. The various ways in which the earth and/or civilisation can be destroyed, long before the demise of the universe, are shown to present even more obstacles to the acceptance of orthodox religious dogmas.

The future evolution of humankind is referred to as a fascinating concept, and the projections of Dougal Dixon in his book *Man after Man* are described in terms of forthcoming genetic manipulation. This, it is pointed out, is something that the pre-Copernican religions had not even considered.

CHAPTER FOUR

Contingency

COULD THE UNIVERSE HAVE BEEN DIFFERENT?

In 1986, Richard Dawkins wrote a book entitled *The Blind Watchmaker*. The idea was to explain the mystery of complex design with respect to living systems. As a rather Calvinistic atheist, Dawkins is at pains to demolish the idea of the 'Conscious Designer'. To do this he uses as his anvil a famous treatise by the eighteenth-century theologian William Paley and for his hammer the works of Charles Darwin. He begins with the famous passage from Paley's *Natural Theology*:

> 'In crossing a heath suppose I pitch my foot against a stone and were asked how the stone came to be there; I might possibly answer that, for anything I knew to the contrary, it had lain there for ever: nor would it perhaps be very easy to show the absurdity of this answer. But suppose I had found a watch upon the ground and it should be inquired how the watch happened to be in that place; I should hardly think of the answer which I had given before, that for anything I knew the watch might always have been there.'

After describing the precision and intricacy with which the watch was fashioned, Paley concludes that if we found such an object upon the heath even if we did not know how it came into existence we would be forced to admit:

> 'That the watch must have had a maker: that there must have existed, at some time and at some place or other, an artificer or artificers, who formed it for the purpose which we found it actually to answer; who comprehended its construction, and designed its use.'

Paley then goes on to compare the watch with the works of nature, stating:

> 'Every indication of contrivance, every manifestation of design, which existed in the watch, exists in the works of nature; with the difference, on the side of nature, being greater or more, and that in a degree which exceeds all computation.'

According to Dawkins, Paley's argument, although presented with beautiful and reverent descriptions of the dissected machinery of life and made with passionate sincerity informed by the best biological arguments of his day, is nevertheless totally wrong. The only watchmaker in nature is the blind force of physics, albeit applied in a very special way.

Dawkins' Argument Contested

But Dawkins is throwing a hostage to fortune. The sceptic can well ask, 'Why should it be applied in such a special way if no design was intended?' The special way consists of Darwin's Law of Natural Selection. Natural selection appears to operate without any special purpose, as Dawkins shows by many examples. But, as our sceptic might say, one of the products is Richard Dawkins and this product has a definite purpose, even if it is to demonstrate to us that there is no such thing as purpose in nature.

Charles Darwin

This seems to illustrate a rather strange aspect of nature. First, we have natural selection producing without purpose some highly sophisticated life-forms, all of which are themselves very purposeful. In fact, purposefulness seems to be one of the main outcomes of natural selection; for surely only those species made up of individuals with the purposeful intention to survive would survive. For example, predators that lost the purposeful intention of hunting would soon become extinct. When we come to the highest life-form on this planet, mankind, purpose takes on a much broader sweep than mere survival. We have the arts, philosophy, architecture, economics and many other forms of purposeful activities. While this does not necessarily validate Paley's argument from design, it does not invalidate it either. Who is to say that the whole panoply of natural selection, not only on this planet, but possibly on millions of others also, is without purpose? It is rather like having one piece of a vast jigsaw puzzle from which we try to guess the construction of the finished picture. It seems that the whole question is an open one and that we have to go much farther in investigating it.

I think that Dawkins paints on too limited a canvas to be utterly convincing. As Freeman Dyson states in his book *Disturbing the Universe*, the idea of chance is just a cover for our ignorance.

Paley's Argument Extended

The real basis of Paley's argument rests upon the question: 'Is the universe contingent?' (– i.e. could it have been different?) If it is contingent, is it also unique? Why, for instance, do gravity and electricity obey the inverse square law? Could it have been an inverse cube law had the universe developed differently? If the universe is contingent then we have to explain why the universe is such that observers like ourselves become an integral part of it. If it is not contingent then we have to explain why the values of the various constants of nature are necessary (the only ones possible) as well as sufficient to explain our existence. We must look at the case for and against the uniqueness of the universe, a very difficult task, because observationally we have only one universe to hand, and it is hard to make a compelling case using a sample of one.

A Brief History of the Universe and the Measurement of Time

Let us outline a brief history of the universe from the time of the Big Bang to the present day. Steven Weinberg gives a much more detailed and technical account in his book *The First Three Minutes*.

As Einstein has shown, time is a variable quantity depending on velocity and acceleration and the frame of the observer. In calculating the history of the universe, the time system employed is known as 'proper time'. It is defined as 'time kept by a clock moving along in the frame of the observer and not in motion relative to it in any way, nor experiencing a different gravitational field'. The age of the universe is that measured by a hypothetical observer who expands with the universe from the initial singularity to the present time. This is the only meaningful and unambiguous concept of time that can be used to measure the age of the universe.

In the first second of the Big Bang as the universe rapidly expands, the particles of matter and anti-matter (protons and anti-protons, electrons and positrons) would have been created and annihilated, leaving a small excess of matter particles with a great deal of electro-magnetic radiation (photons). The reason for this is that when two photons collide they can disappear and form two or more material particles, providing that each photon has energy equal to the rest energy of each particle. This can be deduced from Einstein's famous equation; 'rest energy equals the mass times the square of the speed of light' ($E = mc^2$). When particles of opposite electrical charge (matter and anti-matter) converge, the opposite process takes place and the particles will disappear, their energy now being in the form of photons. During a period of about a minute to twelve minutes, the universe starts to cool. The remaining excess of matter particles will be responsible for the formation of hydrogen, helium and deuterium (heavy hydrogen) atoms; and for about the next ten thousand years the universe would be matter-dominated but still strongly coupled with the bombarding radiation. After about three hundred thousand years, when the universe has cooled down to about 3,000 degrees K, and the rate of expansion has slowed, the radiation and matter de-couple and the universe becomes transparent. This is the time referred to, when observing the cosmic microwave background. After one to two billion years, the formation of galaxies commences. There is a region of dispute as to whether primeval stars formed first and then formed galaxies by gravitational attraction, or whether proto-galaxies of hot gas formed first and then the stars formed within them, but in either case we can reckon on about four billion years before the first stars appear. These are hydrogen-burning stars that make helium in their interiors by nuclear fusion. They then proceed to make the heavier elements, carbon, oxygen, etc., by further fusion. Eventually, when these first stars run out of fuel to burn, their central regions are mainly composed of chromium, manganese, iron, cobalt and nickel. They then implode by gravitational collapse to very dense dwarf stars, even more dense pulsars or the ultimate light-retaining black holes, depending on their mass. The outer layers are ejected in the process, spreading a small amount of the heavy elements into space, together with the hydrogen and helium. These exploding stars are known as novae, or in extreme cases, supernovae. After about ten billion years the next generation of stars forms, this time containing some of the heavier elements from the surrounding debris. Thus, planets like our own can form around them. Our planet was formed about four billion years ago and the first microscopic single cell life-forms (prokaryotes) came into being about three billion years ago. The advent of complex multicellular organisms only took place about 550,000,000 years ago. The evolution of man himself occurred about 2,000,000 years ago and recorded history only started around 7,000 years ago. This whole process appears to be governed by the existing laws of physics incorporating the four fundamental forces: gravity, nuclear bonding (the strong force), the force governing radioactive decay (the weak force), and the electro-magnetic force. These four forces are so finely tuned that a tiny deviation from any one of them could, and almost certainly would, preclude the formation of life in the universe.

Special Conditions for the Formation of Life

In addition to the laws of physics there are the initial conditions obtaining at the time of the Big Bang to consider. Let us examine some of the very special factors that are necessary for the formation of life. There is a very long list of such factors.

1 One of the first prerequisites is that the universe starts out as very smooth, but not absolutely smooth since that would prohibit any formation of galaxies, and hence of ourselves. There are several theoretical scenarios for the era of galaxy formation. All of them must postulate the existence of primordial fluctuations in the radiation and matter i.e. within about the first ten thousand years of existence. The amplitude of these fluctuations would have to be very small and limited to between about 0.01 per cent and 0.001 per cent of the background temperature. If they were too large then the universe would consist only of massive black holes and life could not exist. If they were too small then gravity would not be able to form the stars and galaxies that we now observe. Hence, a very precise measurement of the primordial fluctuations is needed to ensure life-forming galaxies. The reason why and how the Big Bang started in precisely the right way to produce galaxies, and hence us, is a matter of some dispute among cosmologists. It seems that establishing uniformity is required as one of the initial conditions of the Big Bang. It is undoubtedly true that this is a very special condition that, in addition to many other such conditions, could be held by some to validate Paley's argument.

2 For matter to exist at very early times, when the background temperature was in excess of a billion degrees, there must have been a slight excess of matter over anti-matter. If this were not the case then all the matter and anti-matter would have annihilated, forming a purely radiation-dominated universe, and therefore we would not exist. Calculations using both the conservation of energy and the conservation of nuclear particles (baryon number) show that the excess of matter over anti-matter was about one part in a billion. This leaves us with just the right amount of matter to form the present observed universe. Too much matter and the universe would have collapsed and burnt out before enough time could have elapsed for us to come into existence. Too little and there would not be enough to form the stars and galaxies by gravitational attraction. Again, we would not exist.

3 In addition to the above detailed matter/anti-matter annihilation; the remaining matter particles (neutrons and protons, etc.) would be forming the elements of various types of hydrogen and helium essential for star formation. Helium needs neutrons to fuse with protons for its nucleus. It has been calculated that for helium to form, the temperature would have to drop from about six billion to one billion degrees in just about eleven minutes. If it is too slow then all the neutrons would decay into protons and electrons and no helium could form. If it is too fast, then the slow reaction to form helium would not take place and we would have no helium. In either case, there would be no stars and no observers.

4 After star formation has taken place, there is still the need for heavy elements before life itself can form on orbiting planets. In particular, we need the element of carbon. This is because of the very large number of compounds that it can form, and its willingness to combine with many other elements, to provide the necessary basis for the complexity that is essential to living organisms. Carbon can also form long and complex molecules of great variety by virtue of its bonding qualities. Life requires many chemical potentialities, for instance, in obtaining, storing and transporting energy as well as synthesising the building blocks of the cell. In addition, there is a need to replicate the DNA and copy the genetic blueprint to give proteins. This chemical potential is easily available in carbon because it combines readily in a stable fashion with hydrogen, oxygen, nitrogen, phosphorus and sulphur, with a few trace elements, like iodine and iron playing a subsidiary part.

Carbon is an element produced in the interior of stars. First of all hydrogen fusion forms helium and then two helium atoms fuse to form beryllium. The fusion of beryllium with a further atom of helium is now required to form carbon. As beryllium is a very short-lived element, the capture of a third helium atom to form carbon has to be very efficient. This can only be the case if the natural internal quantum energy level of this composite body is resonant with (very close to) the average energy found at the centre of a hot star. Furthermore, the reaction caused by the capture of a further helium atom leading away from carbon to oxygen has to be non-resonant or the carbon would be depleted. Fred Hoyle discovered that such is indeed the case. This startling coincidence, if coincidence it is, is responsible for the abundant production of carbon that is dispersed when the star finally explodes. It then joins the other heavy elements when further stars and planets are formed. Without this very special energy level in the centres of hot stars, the universe would consist only of hydrogen and helium and no life could form.

These are just some of the very special conditions and properties necessary for our existence as observers of the universe.

Penrose, Hawking and Others

When discussing the contingency and uniqueness of the universe let us first consider the ideas of two of the major figures in theoretical cosmology, the mathematicians Roger Penrose and Stephen Hawking.

Hawking, author of the best-selling but little-read *A Brief History of Time*, had previously worked with the well-known relativist George Ellis, on their book *The Large Scale Structure of Space-Time*.

In this highly technical book, which also draws on ideas from Roger Penrose and R P Geroch, it is shown that Einstein's General Theory of Relativity leads to two remarkable predictions about the universe.

1 The fate of massive stars is to collapse into what has been described above as black holes, dense structures with such a strong gravitational force that even light cannot escape from them. The actual surface wherein light is trapped is known as the event horizon. A further calculation by Hawking in 1973 showed that due to the quantum uncertainty principle black holes do lose mass very slowly by radiation. Within the event horizon, each of these structures will contain a singularity. A singularity is a point with zero volume and infinite density. Of course, a point with such impossible characteristics cannot exist. What it really means is a point where the equations of general relativity and all the normal laws

of physics break down. In one sense, it can be thought of as an edge or boundary of space-time.

2   There is a singularity in our past that constitutes in some sense the beginning of the universe. In other words, if we consider any event in the universe to be denoted by four co-ordinates, three of space and one of time, then all four would be zero at this point.

Previously Stephen Hawking and Roger Penrose had worked together to prove theorems about the presence of singularities in wide classes of solutions to the equations of general relativity. However, they have diverged in their ideas about time, the nature of quantum reality, and the special contingency factors of the universe. Hawking considers that the initial conditions of the universe were necessary, while Penrose, in his book *The Emperor's New Mind*, argues that such conditions were extremely precise with respect to the total entropy of the universe, and hence were contingent. If we construct a space containing all the possible initial states of the universe, Penrose has calculated that, were the Creator armed with a pin to single out a spot denoting the state of our actual universe, then the accuracy of the Creator's aim must be to one part in a hundred billion raised to the 123rd power. Without wishing to denigrate the Creator's abilities in this respect, Penrose argues that it is one of the duties of scientists to search for physical laws that explain, or at least describe in some coherent way, the nature of the phenomenal accuracy of both the constants of physics, and their mutual relationships, that we observe in the natural world. We need a new scientific law to explain these special boundary conditions of the initial state of the universe.

Hawking's approach discards any idea of a Creator. Using the methods of quantum cosmology, which predicts the very high probability of a closed universe (see Hawking, *A Brief History of Time*, Chapter Eight, p137, and *The Nature of Space and Time*, Chapter Five, p98), Hawking calculates that as we look back towards the origin of the universe, a simple mathematical transformation causes the time co-ordinate to become a fourth space co-ordinate, hence avoiding the initial singularity in time. Without such a time singularity, the universe cannot be said to have commenced its existence at any particular time. It would be self-contained and unaffected by any external factors. It would be neither created nor destroyed; it would just exist. This eliminates both the boundary and the boundary conditions for the origin of the universe.

This is a very elegant solution to the singularity problem. Unfortunately, this theory is purely mathematical since there is no direct physical evidence for such a transformation of the time co-ordinate, and, moreover, nobody has the slightest idea of what would constitute such evidence. What the theory can do is to make certain predictions, which if not fulfilled, would eliminate the theory. For example, Hawking claims that the isotropic expansion of the universe is predicted by the 'no boundary' condition, and is confirmed by the observations of the smoothness of the microwave background.

Hawking at one time considered that the beginning of the expansion of a closed, no-boundary universe would have to be like its end. But after consultation with Don Page, of Penn State University, and Raymond Laflamme, one of his students, he accepted that the time asymmetry of increasing entropy had somehow to be explained. This he did by the conjecture that the initial perturbations in a short period were heavily damped while the final perturbations can be very large without significant damping. In other words, the universe started its expansion in a smooth and ordered state but in its contracting state, it will be in a state of complete disorder. This implies that intelligent life could only exist in its expanding stage, which is why we observe the universe to be expanding.

A further problem with the above argument is that, according to all the latest observations and calculations, the universe itself is not closed but open. Indeed, there appears to exist only about ten per cent of the mass necessary to close the universe. This of course could change with future observations but at the moment poses a rather significant objection.

Penrose's acceptance of the existence of the initial singularity could invoke a Creator as sufficient but not necessary. Other states of entropy could also give rise to life and consciousness, possibly with a greater economy of energy. It would seem, according to Penrose, that if there were a Creator, we were not His main concern, and indeed could have arisen as a mere by-product of His Designer-universe.

This could make us view Paley's watch in a less sceptical light than Dawkins does, although there are many scientists apart from Penrose and Hawking who are attempting to solve these cosmological problems without postulating the need for a Designer. The speculations in these attempts are ingenious, but sometimes lead to a form of mysticism that most scientists, including myself, find somewhat obscure when used in a scientific context.

Summary

This chapter starts with a discussion of Richard Dawkin's book *The Blind Watchmaker*. It examines the argument from design of William Paley. Dawkins concludes that in the light of Darwinian evolution Paley's argument is fallacious. We proceed to show that such a conclusion is possibly premature when the whole universe is taken into account.

A brief history of the universe, from the 'Big Bang' until the present time, is presented. Questions of the contingency and uniqueness of the universe are raised and some of the necessary conditions for the formation of life in the universe are described.

The incredibly small probability of these conditions and constants being such as to ensure the development of life is given as one argument for the existence of a God or Designer.

The views of Roger Penrose and Stephen Hawking, concerning the origin and fate of the universe, are expounded and shown to diverge. Penrose accepts the possibility, but not necessarily the probability, of a God. Hawking, on the other hand, postulates the 'no boundary' theory of quantum cosmology to dispense with any idea of a Creator. A brief outline of this theory is given, together with certain objections.

We conclude that in the light of scientific evidence, Paley's argument from design retains some validity, although in a much broader sense than he imagined.

Chapter Five

Boundaries

One of the methods by which cosmologists could theoretically dispose of the Designer universe is the concept of the multiverse or 'many universes'; each with different physical laws and initial conditions. Within an infinite or even a very large random ensemble of such universes, statistically there must be some, however sparse, that have the conditions for life to develop. This idea I will describe as the 'random solution'.

The Many Worlds Theory

One such theory is the 'Many-Worlds' interpretation of quantum physics originally proposed by the particle physicist H Everett. In quantum physics sub-atomic particles are described by a wave function in which the particle is in superposition (the same particle in potentially different positions simultaneously). Under observation, the wave function collapses and a specific position becomes well defined. According to Everett, the universe itself is a closed system in a pure quantum state with terms in superposition. These terms form branches, each of which is a branch of the universe as a whole and as real as any other branch. In every branch, there is a relative state of each observer with sensori-neural apparatus and corresponding consciousness exhibiting the properties appropriate to that branch. This idea can be extended to a wave function of the universe which would also include an infinite number of branches that do not have the necessary conditions for life to develop, and hence no observers. In which case, without observation, the wave functions would not collapse and everything would remain in an indeterminate state. This leads to an enormous number of universes co-existing without interacting, an idea used by the author Jorge Luis Borges in his short story 'The Garden of Forking Paths'. In it he describes a labyrinth-cum-novel devised by an imaginary Chinese sage. Ts'ui Pen, in which time forks perpetually toward innumerable futures. The story's imaginary translator writes:

> ' "The Garden of Forking Paths" is an enormous riddle, or parable, whose theme is time…an incomplete but not false image of the universe…. In contrast to Newton or Schopenhauer, Ts'ui Pen did not believe in a uniform absolute time. He believed in an infinite series of times, in a growing, dizzying net of divergent, convergent and parallel times. This network of times which approached one another, forked, broke off, or were unaware of one another for centuries, embraces all possibilities of time…'

Variations on the theme recur throughout Borges' work.

I personally find it difficult to believe in an infinite number of co-existing universes in some of which we may be dead while still alive in others. This may well be brute prejudice but there have been some powerful, highly technical criticisms of this theory by J S Bell and others that focus upon the indefiniteness (mentioned above), even in many of the branches containing observers. In other words, some of the branches would contain indefinite values of macroscopic dynamical variables, which we never see. For example, we never see a pointer on a dial suspended between pointing up and pointing down, or an object suspended between being stationary and moving. Bell has pointed out in addition, that the equal reality of all the branches wipes out the distinction between potentiality and actuality that is central to decision-making, to ethical choice and to all practical activity. Indeed, he says, '...if such a theory were taken seriously it would hardly be possible to take anything seriously.' Apart from these social implications, there is also the boundary problem discussed below. What would separate such universes?

Another form of the many-worlds theory, that at first sight seems more plausible, is the construction and destruction of universes in serial, rather than parallel time: the expansion and then contraction of a universe from and to a singularity, followed by the expansion and contraction of the next one with different physical constants, and so on ad infinitum. In fact, it would really be one universe, undergoing different cycles of existence. One of these cycles is bound to be one that fulfils the right conditions for life to emerge. In fact, there would be an infinite number of them as a subclass of universes, and our universe would be one of them. This neatly does away with any teleological or metaphysical reasoning for the existence of a Creator. This theory, however, does not at the moment, accord with all the observations. It appears that there is not enough matter in the universe to cause a contraction although there is still some debate on this subject, as previously discussed. In addition to the observational problem of the oscillating universe, there is a theoretical problem. There could not have been an infinite number of previous oscillations since in each cycle the radiation produced by the stars would increase the photon to baryon (radiation to matter) ratio in the universe. A rough calculation gives at the most about 100 previous cycles so we are left with the problem of the creation of the universe at a specific time and a limited number of cycles to explain any special initial conditions. This still leaves us with Paley's watch.

The Structure of Boundaries

The whole concept of separate universes, either simultaneous or serial, leads to the problem of the boundaries between them. What sort of structure could these boundaries possibly have? If these universes exist as truly separate entities, the boundaries between them must have some structure. A similar problem existed in ancient times concerning the boundaries between earth, heaven and hell. This was simply solved in terms of the sky, the ground and below ground, but with modern concepts of cosmology, such simplicity is no longer possible.

One can think of the problem in the following way. Existence implies structure of some sort but structure also implies existence. Even a hallucination has a structure in the form of neuronal activity in the brain of the person hallucinating. The same is true of literary and artistic works. If existence implies structure and if we accept the existence of separate objects in the universe, then boundaries of some sort must separate such objects, which brings us back to Aristotle's definition of form given in Chapter One. If other separate universes exist in parallel with our own, there must exist boundaries between them. These boundaries cannot be formed in space or time since space-time is a self-contained, integral part of each separate universe. What is the answer? It could well be that the other universes are not truly separate. For example, the serial universes mentioned above, or the 'bubble' universes described in the following section. Total separation, as in Everett's 'Many Worlds' theory, could well lead to a form of mysticism that is antithetical to the scientific method.

Do we have any observational evidence that other universes exist? On the face of it, we do not. Nevertheless, we do have evidence of a conceptual universe that appears to have an objective existence and describes, or even shapes, the physical universe in which we live. That this is so may be seen from the concepts and ideas of mathematics. For example, the geometry of the conic sections discovered by Apollonius and his successors as an exercise in pure geometry in about 230BC turned out not only to describe all the various orbits in Newton's Law of Universal Gravitation but also described the exponential and trigonometric concepts of statistics and electrical engineering. There are many other examples of what at first seemed pure mathematical discoveries, for example, matrices, Reimanian geometry, and complex numbers, that later were seen to describe the physics of the universe. The whole idea is reinforced when we consider the effect of music upon both our emotions and our aesthetic sensibilities. Music is on one level a branch of mathematics, which can convey its beauty and elegance to those of us whose knowledge of pure mathematics is only rudimentary. This would imply that a dual conceptual universe of such mathematical forms exists which can describe various aspects of our universe. If such is the case for mathematics, it is not inconceivable that similar absolutes should exist for good and evil, beauty, justice, etc.

Such Platonic arguments can be used to support a theistic view of the universe, but they do not necessarily validate the Western Religions. Indeed, Max Horkheimer (1895–1973), a sociologist of the Frankfurt school saw God as a necessary ideal for society. Without the idea of God, he considered such absolutes to be subjective illusions. Ethics becomes a matter of practicality and justice the law of the strongest. There is no reason why we should not hate or murder if it serves our purpose. Religion, then, is an inner feeling that there is a God of some sort and that the injustice suffered in this world should not be the last word. It is a chilling thought that such inner feelings do not necessarily imply validity. These ideas will be discussed further in Chapter Seven.

Inflation

One theory that, if true, could in one form effectively dispose of the Designer universe without any mystical implications, is that of the 'inflationary universe' formulated by Alan H Guth. The idea is that at a very early stage the universe underwent a brief stage of superluminal (faster than light) exponentially fast expansion. Now, according to Einstein's Special Theory of Relativity, nothing with real mass can travel faster through space than light in a vacuum, since the energy involved would approach an infinite value. The superluminal inflation is averred possible, because it is assumed that as it is space itself that is expanding, there is no transportation of energy involved. This it seems could have been caused by a super-cooled phase transition at an earlier time. A phase transition is a change of state of the relevant system, for example, the change of state of ice to water or water to steam. In the inflationary case, the change would be from one grand unified force in being at the time of the Big Bang to some or all of the four forces of physics mentioned above that we know today. Technical details of the theory are well explained in Guth's book, *The Inflationary Universe.*

There are two major problems that this theory purports to solve:

1   The problem of *flatness.* By this we mean that the actual density of matter in the universe should be equal to, or very close to, the critical density, which is the density that would put the universe right on the edge between eternal expansion and eventual collapse. The ratio between the actual density and the critical density is normally referred to by the Greek letter Ω (omega). If W started out at exactly unity then it would remain there forever. If Ω differed from 1, even by an infinitesimal amount, then the deviation from 1 would increase with time, and today it would be very far from unity. In fact, the latest observed estimates, which we discussed in the last chapter, lie between about 0 and 1, which indeed is very close to the critical density. For this to be the case W would have had to start from within a hundred-thousand billionth of unity. This could be interpreted as a very special value, deliberately chosen to ensure our existence. In the inflation scenario, however, the value

could have started at any number, because the effect of gravity is reversed during the inflationary period, and Guth claims that all the equations describing the development of the universe are changed by inflation, causing Ω to be driven swiftly towards unity. The standard cosmological expansion would resume after the end of inflation, but the value of Ω would remain very close to 1, right up to the present day. This testable result seems to fit well with the latest observations.

2 The *horizon problem*. As the universe in the Big Bang theory is of a finite age, there is a maximum distance that light could have travelled since its beginning. This is called the horizon distance. Since nothing can travel faster than light in a vacuum, this distance is an upper bound on the transfer of any information within the present age of the universe. The microwave cosmic background radiation gives us a picture of the universe at the age of between 200,000 to 300,000 years, when radiation de-coupled from matter, and the universe became transparent to light. As we have discussed before, this background is incredibly uniform to an amplitude of 0.001 per cent. Since light, or any other information, has not had the time, since the beginning of the universe, to reach even a small fraction of the cosmic background, how has such uniformity been established? Certainly not by the zeroth law of thermodynamics mentioned in the last chapter.

The inflationary theory solves this problem, since before the period of rapid inflation, the universe was small enough to allow the spread of information to reach all parts of the present observed universe, allowing it to reach a uniform temperature in the time available.

The Steady State Resurrected

This leads to Guth's concept of bubble universes as a result of the inflation scenario. To describe this scenario we need to examine the inflation theory in a little more depth. Guth has compared the phase transition of the early universe to the phase transition of water into steam. When water boils, its temperature rises to slightly above boiling point: bubbles of steam then form randomly in the hot water, growing and absorbing energy from its surroundings, thus preventing the water temperature from rising much above boiling point. The heat energy absorbed by the growing bubbles is used to convert water to steam, which is the higher energy phase. The phase transition of the early universe is similar except that the temperature is falling instead of rising.

Consider the temperature falling well below that needed for the phase transition of the universal force into the four forces, already remarked upon, which we know exist today. Also, consider that the required phase transition has not yet taken place, in much the same way as super-cooled water can exist as a liquid below the normal freezing temperature provided there is no disturbance. Physicists refer to this state of the universe as the 'false vacuum'. Because such a state depends upon a highly technical and as yet a completely theoretical concept called the 'Higgs field' (see Guth's *The Inflationary Universe*), the false vacuum has a very peculiar property. It has a constant energy density irrespective of how much the volume changes, unlike a normal gas in which the energy density decreases with increasing volume. This means that as the volume expands the total energy increases, acting against the expansion, which in turn creates a negative pressure (suction). Since gravity can be induced by pressure according to Einstein's equations of general relativity, the induced gravity will be repulsive instead of attractive because the pressure is negative. Hence the exponential expansion.

This false vacuum will not last forever in its pure state. It will start to decay in a process known as quantum tunnelling, instigating a phase change into bubbles containing the lower four-force phase that we know at present.

In this case, it is calculated that bubbles of the new phase would begin to form randomly as the false vacuum decays. Each bubble universe would expand at almost the speed of light, but as the bubble universes form, the exponential expansion of the remaining false vacuum would continue. The rate of expansion is calculated to be much faster than the rate of decay, so once expansion starts it goes on forever. The number of bubble universes then tends to infinity. There is unfortunately no possibility of any observational confirmation as to whether ours is the first or the twentieth-billionth universe in the series.

In this process, it seems that the physical constants and the initial conditions for each universe could be the same, each tending to the critical density but later each diverging into open or closed universes. Life, it seems, would go on forever in at least some of the continually created universes. There is no problem with boundaries here since the boundary between universes is the false vacuum, which, in theory anyway, is well defined. The question of the origin of the universe remains and Paley's argument from design, at least in the cosmological sense, still stands.

Guth advances the argument that perhaps there never was a beginning to the universe. Perhaps inflation has been an eternal phenomenon. This does away with any pre-inflationary phase and postulates that the false vacuum has always been with us. In this case, there is only a one-way phase change from the higher to the lower phase of the present universe or universes as the false vacuum continues its infinite decay process. Such an idea brings much comfort to the exponents of the steady state theory. It will satisfy their idea of an endless universe in which the problem of an origin disappears. It could be argued, indeed, that such an ensemble of so-called bubble universes is really only one universe with a specific structure that includes all the lower phase bubbles.

This does not dismiss the argument from design advanced by

Paley, even if such were the case. There is, it seems, nothing to stop an eternal Designer or God from creating an eternal universe with all the special conditions necessary for the formation of life ad infinitum. But it does pose great difficulties for the Western pre-Copernican religions with respect to their ideas of a judgement day, the second coming, the Messiah, etc.

It appears in all probability that eternal inflation in the past is not the case. If it were, then any open universe would have expanded to infinity and suffered the heat death. This contradicts the idea of an infinitely inflating false vacuum state; hence, there must have been a singularity at some finite time in the past. It does not contradict eternal inflation into the future, of course, and could place the original singularity at an indefinite time in the past. Arvind Borde and Alexander Vilenkin give a mathematical proof of this in their paper, 'Eternal Inflation and the Initial Singularity'. If all the bubble universes were closed then the question remains undecided because the universes would expand for some finite time and then contract to the original fireball. This is not a likely scenario, firstly because the critical density itself implies a flat universe with infinite but slowing expansion and secondly most of our present observations indicate an open or flat universe.

Martin Rees, in his book *Before the Beginning*, captures the essence of modern cosmology. Without being in the slightest bit technical, it explores many difficult and exotic areas and explains them with great clarity to the layperson. Discussing the inflationary universe described in the previous paragraphs, he examines the idea that our universe is only one of a large ensemble of bubble universes. To escape from the Designer argument he postulates that each bubble universe could have cooled down differently, introducing different physical constants and initial conditions. In other words, our universe is not unique. This is an idea that many cosmologists consider one of the non-Designer solutions to the existence of cosmologists. Andrei Linde, in an article in *Scientific American*, considers the case where there could be several fields involved in addition to the Higgs field already mentioned. The freezing-out of these fields at different energy states could possibly produce such varied universes. Unfortunately, the present level of knowledge of high-energy particle physics does not allow us to formulate a convincing scenario for this speculation.

Inflation Contested

Not everybody accepts the inflation theory. Roger Penrose writes in his book, *The Large, the Small and the Human Mind*:

> 'The argument (that the rapid inflation of the universe leads to flatness) does not do what it is supposed to do:- what you would expect in this initial state, if it were randomly chosen, would be an horrendous mess and, if you expand this mess by a huge factor, it still remains an horrendous mess. In fact it looks worse and worse the more it expands, so the argument by itself does not explain why the universe is so uniform.'

In other words, he disputes that with inflation the equations would drive the value of Ω to the value of unity. Such criticism by Penrose has to be taken seriously. A further problem with inflation, brought up by Alan Guth himself, is the fact that the mathematical field necessary for driving inflation has to be added ad hoc to any of the grand unified theories under consideration for the early stages of the Big Bang This makes the inflation theory look rather contrived. As Guth says, 'We still appear to be a long way from pinning down the details of the particle physics that underlie inflation.'

Coles and Ellis, in their book *Is the Universe Open or Closed?*, also consider cases where inflation does not necessarily drive the density to the critical value. One way of determining if inflation took place would be the detection of gravitational waves, that is waves in the actual structure of space-time that would have been set off by the initial inflation scenario. The problem with such detection is the extreme faintness of the waves themselves. So far, nobody has been able to detect such waves convincingly.

The COBE Discovery

One prediction from the inflationary scenario that has been observed is the scale invariance of the post-inflation perturbations in the cosmic microwave background. This means that the perturbations, i.e. the very slight differences in the temperature of this background, should cover areas of all sizes but with the same area of sky occupied by each class size. This would happen because the slight primordial perturbations generated in the early stages of inflation would be stretched to greater areas than those generated later. It has been calculated that such scale invariance would in fact lead to the structure of the universe that we observe today, with galaxies, clusters and super clusters of galaxies. Scale invariant perturbations of about .001 per cent of the background were indeed detected by George Smoot and his team using the Cosmic Background Explorer (COBE) satellite in 1992. Unfortunately, the mechanism suggested for scale invariant perturbations bears an uncomfortable resemblance to Penrose's objections to the inflation theory. However, the very discovery of these small perturbations is an extraordinary technical achievement and gives additional confirmation of the 'Big Bang' origin of the universe, inflation or no inflation.

Summary

This chapter is devoted to the idea of the multiverse or many-universes. It is explained that such a theory could dispense with a Creator, because if there is a vast or even infinite number of separate universes, then statistically there must be somewhere the conditions would be right for life to develop.

Attention is given to the problem of the boundaries between such separate universes, hence the title of the chapter. In this vein Everett's 'Many Worlds' theory is explained.

The concept of a closed universe contracting to explode again into another 'Big Bang', giving an infinite series of serial universes with different constants and conditions, is shown to be unlikely. The pre-existence of mathematics is demonstrated to give some credence to Plato's world of archetypes.

The existence of the boundaries between separate universes is shown to give rise to physical difficulties if the universes are truly separate.

Alan Guth's inflationary universe is discussed in detail and his concept of 'bubble universes' explained as an expanded form of the 'Steady State Theory. An idea endorsed by such well-known cosmologists as Martin Rees and Andrei Linde, who have introduced further developments of their own.

Roger Penrose's objections to inflation are described together with the findings of the COBE satellite, which, ironically, confirm the predictions of both inflation, and Penrose's objection to it.

Different Universes each with its own spacetime.
What separates them?

Separate Universes

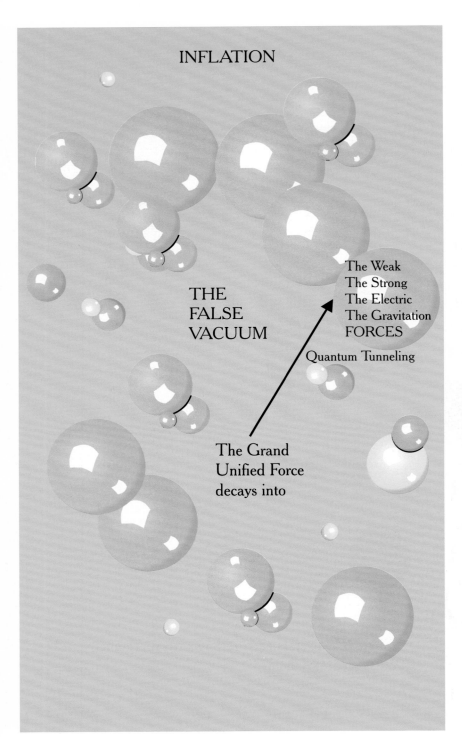

Bubble Universes

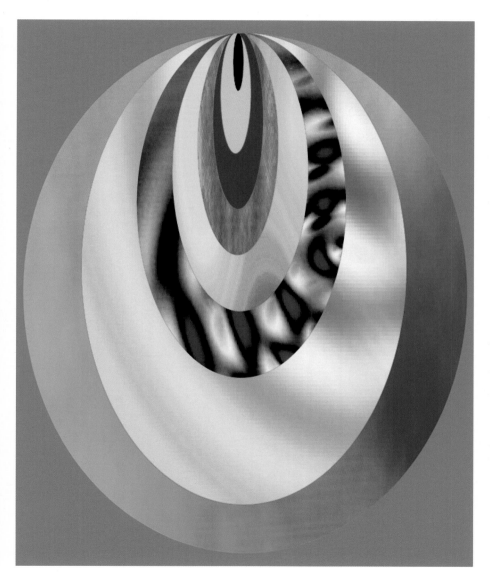

UNIVERSES WITHIN UNIVERSES WITHIN UNIVERSES

Russian Doll Universes

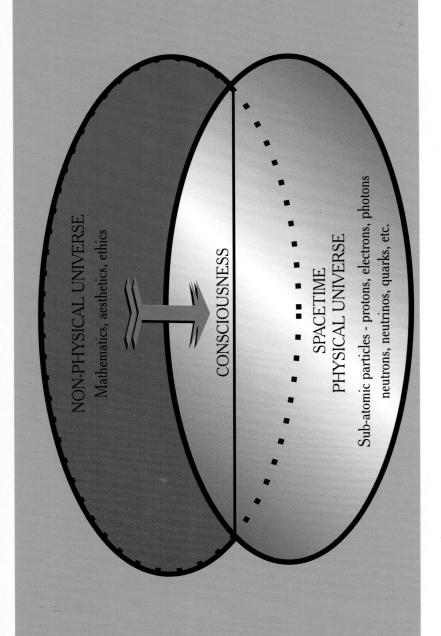

NON-PHYSICAL UNIVERSE
Mathematics, aesthetics, ethics

CONSCIOUSNESS

SPACETIME
PHYSICAL UNIVERSE

Sub-atomic particles - protons, electrons, photons
neutrons, neutrinos, quarks, etc.

Intersecting Universes

CHAPTER SIX

The Anthropic Principle

WAS THE UNIVERSE MADE FOR US?

The dispute as to whether we are the result of a Designer-universe, as Paley suggests, or the minor by-product of mindless forces as Dawkins suggests, has led the cosmologist Brandon Carter to limit the Copernican Principle by an Anthropic Principle. There are two main manifestations of this principle, although they can be subdivided if required.

The Weak Anthropic Principle (WAP) states that what we observe must be compatible with our existence. We see a universe with stars and planets because we live on a planet. We see a universe with carbon atoms because we are constructed from carbon atoms. We see a universe billions of years old because it took billions of years to develop creatures that can think about the structure of the universe. In other words, the very form of our existence biases our observations. This is the principle endorsed by the evolutionary biologist Stephen Jay Gould. We are here because the conditions happened to be right for our evolution. Thus our presence is merely fortuitous, implying that such conditions are not contingent or that we observe a highly unlikely statistical convolution of such conditions.

Set against this we have the Strong Anthropic Principle (SAP), which states that the universe *must* have those properties that would allow life to develop at some stage. This gives a metaphysical tone to the argument, implying that the existence of the conditions for life to emerge is a result of design on the part of a Creator, who desires the creation of sentient life (Natural Theology).

Gerald Schroeder, God's Spin Doctor

One strong advocate of the reconciliation of religion and cosmology is the scientist and author Gerald L Schroeder. He has written books entitled *Genesis and the Big Bang* and *The Science of God*. In them, he claims to have discovered a correspondence between the chapter of Genesis in the Torah and the ideas of modern cosmology. To confirm his ideas, he concentrates a great deal on scientific details and the writings of ancient Hebrew scholars. Unfortunately, the ideas and language of the Torah have a certain authoritative rigidity, which do not adjust very well to the uncertainties and speculations of science.

Schroeder has attempted to reconcile the two by a free interpretation of the Torah together with a somewhat rigid presentation of the science. He refers in particular to the writings of the thirteenth-century scholar Nahmanides, whom he describes as having believed that a full understanding of the origins of the universe was contained in the Bible as received by Moses. Schroeder tells us that: 'The information was written either explicitly or by hints taken in some instances from the very form of the written Hebrew text.'

Schroeder's use of such writings is very apt, and he makes some very relevant comparisons of Genesis and aspects of modern cosmology.

In the standard 'Big Bang' model of modern cosmology, the universe appears to have sprung into existence about fifteen billion years ago with an infinite, or almost infinite, temperature and density, and commenced a rapid expansion; thus corresponding to the first sentence in Genesis: 'In the beginning God created the heaven and the earth.'

At this time and shortly afterwards, the intense heat and density ensured that matter could not exist, even as a gas. It must be in a state called plasma, where the atoms are dissociated into electrically charged particles. This plasma absorbs and scatters light strongly, covering the universe in a brilliant but opaque fog. Upon further expansion and cooling, these free particles combine to form atoms of hydrogen and helium. The matter is now stable and no longer reacts strongly with radiation. The universe suddenly becomes transparent, echoing God's command in Genesis 'Let there be light'. This occurred about 300,000 years after the Big Bang when the temperature had cooled to about 3,000 degrees Kelvin.

When we look back at this event we find, with respect to temperature, an incredibly smooth cosmic background radiation, which in the succeeding aeons has cooled to about three degrees Kelvin.

All this Schroeder correctly associates with the descriptions in Genesis. Unfortunately he tends to spoil his argument by trying to make the comparison too literal. For example, he is not content with directly describing the six days of creation as really pertaining to six general periods of time, which is quite an acceptable argument. He attempts to use Einstein's principle of special relativity to posit that there really were six periods of twenty-four hours in the frame of the observer, i.e. God.

Schroeder employs this basic principle to assert that for the time preceding Adam the sequential development of the universe was chosen to be recorded in the Creator's own preferred reference frame. For this, Schroeder has logically chosen the time of the formation of the cosmic background radiation, when matter became stable. He calculates correctly that the time dilation would be proportional to the ratio of the change in temperature of the cosmic background radiation between the time of formation and now. As we have seen, this is about 1,000 ($3,000°K/3°K$). However, Schroeder has erroneously considered a much earlier period as the time of the formation of the cosmic background radiation and used 1,000 billion as his temperature ratio. Dividing this into the approximate age of the universe in proper time i.e. 15 billion years, gives a convenient 5.4 days. Had he used the correct ratio of 1,000 the answer would be 15,000,000 years, which is not so convenient. He could, of course, claim that he meant to use a much earlier time than the formation of the cosmic background radiation, but this would look rather contrived since one could choose any temperature between 3,000°K and infinity and make it fit.

Surely, such sophistry is unnecessary. Even if his calculations were correct he would still be saying, in a roundabout way, that the days of Genesis corresponded to periods of proper time as previously defined.

In *Genesis and the Big Bang*, the argument against the statistical chances of life developing naturally within the time span of the earth's lifetime is accepted as if the whole scientific community is in agreement. That such is not the case is evident from the work of Stuart Kauffman and colleagues on self-organisation and selection in evolution (see Chapter Two). Self-organisation is mentioned, however, in *The Science of God*.

As for his contention that the fossil record disproves Charles Darwin's theory of evolution by natural selection, this almost falls into the trap of the discredited creationist's argument promulgated by religious extremists in the USA. No respectable biologist would accept that evolution by natural selection is a mistaken idea, although certain modifications have been suggested from time to time. Schroeder's contention of a divine evolutionary purpose could still be argued through the laws of probability and the normal distribution, especially if we consider the millions of other planets in the universe. Nevertheless, the explicit intervention of a Creator deliberately causing extinctions, etc. to bring about humankind upon this planet, alone in the whole universe stretches credibility, however much it may correspond with the Torah.

Finally, we come to an example of special pleading par excellence. Schroeder expands upon a remark made by the twelfth-century Jewish philosopher Moses Maimonides. In his *Guide for the Perplexed*, Maimonides says that in the time of Adam there co-existed animals that appeared as humans in shape and intelligence but lacked the soul that differentiates man from the beasts. Where Maimonides obtained this information is not known. It is certainly not mentioned in Genesis. Is it possible that Maimonides may have had some inkling of the existence of Neanderthal man? If so it would be very interesting to find his references, because the first discovery of Neanderthal remains was not made until 1856 in a valley near Dusseldorf, Germany. Although a different species of man, the Neanderthals, who became extinct about 30,000 years ago, were definitely men with brains similar in size to modern man. According to Schroeder, however, the writings of Maimonides gives rise to the concept that 5,700 years ago, Adam, one of the thousands of human creatures roaming this earth, was selected by God as the first creature to be given a soul. This soul was presumably accompanied by neuronal additions to the brain's frontal lobes to accommodate self-consciousness. The rest of the population, it seems, were not men at all. They were animals that looked like men.

This is a very curious idea. I get the impression that the books are written to please the orthodox rabbis who insist upon a literal reading of the Torah. This is a pity because many of Schroeder's arguments make a reasonable case for the existence of a Creator, especially the description of the very special conditions necessary for the formation of life in the universe.

To try to accommodate such well-written books literally to the precepts of a pre-Copernican religious document tends to destroy their credibility. The Torah is true, as all great literature is true, to the imagination and understanding of the human mind.

The Application of the Anthropic Principle

The WAP is really just a statement of observed facts and, at first sight appears to be devoid of relevance. However, it does help us to distinguish those features of the universe that depend on anthropocentric selection from those determined by the action of physical laws. An example would be the resonant production of carbon in the interior of stars as already described. Other examples include Einstein's relativistic mechanics as opposed to the anthropocentric derivation of Newtonian mechanics, or the heliocentric system of Copernicus as opposed to the anthropocentric system of Ptolemy. The WAP can be used to explain the structure of our universe compared to that of many other universes if such universes exist or have existed in the past.

L Smolin made an extension of this principle in 1992. What, he asks, is the mechanism that could lead to the formation of a universe like our own, where the physical constants and the initial conditions are such that life can exist? The WAP itself does not suggest any such mechanism and Smolin attempts to fill this gap.

The Evolution of Universes

His idea is based upon the production of black holes. We have briefly mentioned a black hole as the final collapse of a massive star to such a compact density and with such strong gravitational attraction that even light cannot escape from it. We have also noted that within the black hole there appears to exist a singularity in which all the normal rules of physics break down. One of the very speculative theories regarding singularities is the tunnelling concept: the idea that quantum effects would avoid such a singularity by the creation of an explosion, which in effect would be the Big Bang commencement of a new universe. As this would be inside the event horizon of a black hole, we would never see it. It would in fact be a new region of space-time created by the explosion. We can consider this as a tunnel or wormhole leading to new universe. In theory, such regions could even form within distant parts of our own universe. Smolin uses this concept as the basis of his theory of the evolution of universes by natural selection. He proposes that they rebound with shuffled physical constants and initial conditions in an arbitrary fashion so that, eventually, life-forming universes will come into being.

Some universes, for example, will have parameters that produce stars and hence black holes These black holes then form more universes with reshuffled parameters, some of which contain many stars and black holes and some of which contain much fewer or none. If there are many stars and black holes then other universes, again with different physical parameters, are formed. If there are no black holes and the universe is closed then a further universe will be created on the rebound from final collapse. If such a universe is open then presumably no further universes are formed.

Smolin postulates that originally a universe exists with natural parameters (e.g. the basic constants of particle physics), which according to the physicists, should all be dimensionless numbers of the order of one, i.e. equal to each other. This universe is closed and hence collapses back into a singularity that rebounds with slightly altered parameters and so on until universes containing stars and black holes form, each black hole going on to form more universes, and so on ad infinitum. There is no theory of how the original universe came into being.

If we begin with one such universe, holding to assumptions about the formation of black holes, this single universe could give rise to a large collection of universes, almost all of which have a narrow range of parameters that lead to the maximum production of black holes. This one single universe is not necessarily the first universe. It could have been any universe in a collection with natural parameters. This ensures that eventually some of them will give rise to an enormous collection of universes dominated by those with parameters most likely to produce black holes.

Smolin considers that if almost any change of the physical constants of our present universe result in fewer black holes, then our universe has close to the maximum number of stars and therefore black holes. Since the formation of stars is one of the necessary conditions for the formation of life, then such universes are the ones most likely to harbour life. In other words, the parameters that lead to the maximum number of black holes are also the parameters that lead to the formation of life itself. If we assume that the changes in these parameters from universe to universe are small, establishing a dependency, then a theoretical test becomes possible. From what we know of physics and mathematics, we can attempt to calculate what the effect of slight changes in the parameters would be upon the production of black holes. In his book *The Life of the Cosmos*, Smolin considers that there are at least twenty parameters in elementary particle physics and each one can be either increased or reduced, giving about forty chances to refute the theory. The probability of all forty changes leading to a decrease if the parameters and black hole production are independent of each other is about (1 /1000 billion), which is negligible. This of course assumes that the changes in the parameters, when combined in different ways, do not have unexpected adverse effects. It may be perfectly possible, but highly unlikely, that a change in two or more of the parameters that in themselves lead to a decrease, when combined, would lead to an increase. An example of such a phenomenon can be given from the science of biology. The effects of pressure and anaesthesia interact in this way. Tadpoles cease movement if they undergo exposure to a low concentration of alcohol or to an increase of pressure but when both are applied simultaneously, they swim normally. If such interactions in the physical parameters of the universe are taken into consideration, this could give a probability of many more than forty chances of refutation (at least 380 chances).

Smolin considers the present situation. There are at least eight cases in which either increasing or a decreasing a specific parameter would lead to a dramatic decrease in the number of black holes in the universe. In some cases, it is not possible to predict whether a change would lead to fewer or more black holes. He knows of no cases in where a slight change would lead to a large increase in the number of black holes.

It should be noted that this cosmology deliberately models Darwin's theory of natural selection in his evolutionary concept and provides a useful analogy with Dawkin's argument in *The Blind Watchmaker*. A Designer is no longer necessary since those universes with the most stars and black holes would be ones like ours, containing life-forms as part of the natural selection process. There still remains a problem concerning the origin of these self-selecting universes.

This is a very ingenious theory but contains certain flaws. For instance, we come to the boundary problem again. If a universe is formed within a singularity, how is it separated from the mother universe? Is it still within the singularity or has it in some mysterious way tunnelled into some separate existence? If it is within the singularity then we have the prospect of the Russian Doll Multiverse, i.e. universes within universes. How are these boundaries to be defined? If the new universe is exterior to the singularity, then a problem still exists. Where does it tunnel to if not within our own universe? If it tunnels into our own universe, then we need boundaries between the different universes, each with different physical parameters. This could be similar to those postulated in the inflationary model previously described. How would such boundaries form?

Finally, there is no evidence whatsoever that a singularity would tunnel into the formation of another universe or to anywhere else either. Actually, we do not know anything about the structure of singularities or even whether they exist in the physical world, although mathematically their existence appears to be well defined within general relativity. There could well be some physical quantum process that prevents the formation of such entities without the formation of new universes.

A paper by Rothman and Ellis examines this idea put forward by Smolin. They find it interesting and believe that it opens up new vistas for explanations in cosmology but they also find that it has several problems and obscurities apart from those raised above.

First, they consider the application of biological evolution to cosmological evolution. This, it seems, is not self-evident. The analogy needs to be tested. For instance, in the medieval world an analogy was made between the laws governing the workings of the universe and those governing the attributes of the individual. This resulted in the identification of parts of the body with the planets. Such an analogy is today considered invalid because of the confusion of the two types of operating systems and the lack of any causal influence between them. How is Smolin's proposition to be tested? It may be theoretically testable by mathematical and physical consistency, but it is certainly not amenable to experiment.

Rothman and Ellis next consider some further technical criticisms. Since these criticisms are highly mathematical, I refer the interested reader to their original paper, but the general conclusion is that the tacit assumption of stable long-lived stars with black holes is one that leads to numerous difficulties. It is possible, by varying the initial parameters, to produce a universe with very few stars but many black holes. In this case we would proceed to lifeless universes full of black holes, so other assumptions would have to be made regarding the natural selection evolutionary model. Such a model is certainly a powerful way of producing apparent design from a random basis and could be one way of dispensing with the idea of deliberate creation, thus confirming Dawkin's *Blind Watchmaker* thesis. Nevertheless, the problem of the origin of the universe would remain.

Smolin's book, *The Life of the Cosmos*, mentioned above, is very readable. In it, he goes into great detail, although eschewing mathematics for the sake of the general non-technical reader. He replies to the criticisms of Rothman and Ellis, claiming that they miss a key point. This is that the majority of black holes produced in our universe require the presence of carbon and oxygen. These form clouds of organic molecules shielding cool dense gas from starlight, allowing massive stars to form by gravitational attraction, which eventually go on to become black holes. It is not good enough, he says, to base estimates of star formation and black hole formation rates upon simple models involving only gravitational collapse and cloud fragmentation. They should also involve the role carbon and oxygen play in shielding and cooling the star forming clouds.

From reading Smolin's book I have the impression that there is a strong motivation to dispense with the idea of 'God', an idea he associates with ancient superstition and prejudice. Here I find echoes of *A Free Man's Worship*, an essay by Bertrand Russell. To quote:

> 'So there never was a God, no pilot who made the world by imposing order on chaos and who remains outside, watching and proscribing. And Nietzsche also now is dead. The eternal return, the eternal heat death, are no longer threats, they will never come, nor will heaven. The world will always be here, and it will always be different, more varied, more interesting, more alive, but still always the world in all its complexity and incompleteness. There is nothing behind it, no absolute or platonic world to transcend to. All there is of Nature is what is around us, all there is of Being is relations among real sensible things. All we have of natural law is a world that has made itself. All we may expect of human law is what we can negotiate among ourselves, and what we take as our responsibility. All we may gain of knowledge must be drawn from what we can see with our own eyes. All we may expect of justice is compassion. All we may look up to as judges are each other. All that is possible of Utopia is what we make with our own hands. Pray (sic) let it be enough.'

Here he is at one with Dawkins and Dennett. Unlike Dawkins, Smolin's theory of events that take place within the event horizon of a black hole is not amenable to observation or experiment. Even if it was proved indisputably that the presently observed physical parameters of our universe lead to the maximum production of black holes this doesn't tell us anything about what goes on, if anything, inside black holes.

There is the further conjecture that if his theory is correct then this collection of universes must be subject to time. Based as it is upon Darwinian evolution, time is an essential element; not only time in the broad sense of the space-time of general relativity but time in the Newtonian sense. Newton formulated the following definition of time:

> 'Absolute, true and mathematical time, of itself and by its own true nature, flows uniformly on, without regard to anything external.'

In fact, we now know Newtonian time to be a good approximation to a special case of relativistic space-time in a weak gravitational field with respect to slow relative velocities. This fits Darwinian evolution perfectly. The earth has a very weak gravitational field compared to neutron stars or black holes Forms of life, even when they take to aeroplanes and space rockets, have very slow relative velocities compared to the velocity of light. It is the gradual progress of time that makes evolution by natural selection possible. If this same evolutionary process is to be applied to the formation of universes and each universe contains its own space-time, then we need some overall form of Newtonian time to govern it. Smolin suggests in his book that this super-time is formed from the relative space-time intervals within the universal evolutionary process itself: a form of universal self-organisation. How the intervals of an enormous number of self-reproducing universes organise themselves into a form of Newtonian time is a problem in itself.

This whole concept is an original speculation. It attempts to deal constructively with the problems of the Anthropic Principle and investigates the incredibly fine-tuning of the physical parameters that allow life to develop. In so doing, like most theories, it raises other problems yet to be addressed.

Were We Constructed by a Super Civilisation?

Another relevant paper on this subject is by Edward R Harrison of the University of Massachusetts. He also addresses the possible connection between black holes and intelligent life. He proposes that our universe was created by superior intelligences existing in another physical universe in which the constants of physics are finely tuned and therefore essentially similar to our own. Although this seems more like science fiction than science, it is published in the *Quarterly Journal of the Royal Astronomical Society* and is obviously taken seriously by its editors and referees.

Harrison gives a short description of the fundamental constants of physics and some examples of how only slight variations would rule out the development of life. He then examines the concept that such an intricate network of interlocking critical relations appears to be evidence that the universe has been designed at a fundamental (not superficial) physical level for the benefit of organic life. This would point to a deliberate creation, augmenting Smolin's conjecture regarding the natural selection of universes.

Harrison explores the possibility of creating a universe spanning a 100 billion light years and containing billions of galaxies. He quotes work by Farhi and Guth, who consider how one day it may be possible to form a small black hole of about 10kg mass in the laboratory! (How do you stop it crunching everything in sight?) By careful arrangement, this black hole has an interior that immediately inflates, not in our universe but in a re-entrant bubble-like space-time that is connected to our universe via the umbilical cord originating from the singularity of the black hole. The black hole rapidly evaporates by Hawking radiation and severs the connecting link with the new universe. The offspring universe will inherit the physical constants of the parent universe and thus another life-bearing universe comes into being. Harrison considers that if beings of our limited intelligence can dream up wild and implausible schemes for making universes then beings of a much higher and developed intelligence might actually possess the technique for achieving it. According to Harrison, this theory also explains why man is able to comprehend the universe. He was deliberately programmed to do so, not by a Supreme Being but by a supreme civilisation whose intelligence is far in excess of his own.

The whole point of this idea is to offer a third alternative to the theistic and the random theories of creation. Life itself takes over the creation and cosmogenesis (the origin of the contents of the universe rather than the universe itself) drops out of the religious sphere and becomes a subject amenable to scientific investigation. This still leaves the problem of how it all began. One possibility is an infinite regress of universe creation, which brings us back in principle, although in a different form, to the continuous creation of matter postulated by Hoyle, Bondi and Narlikar. If this were the case then the whole of existence takes on circularity, conforming to the universe of the Jainistic religion of India. They believe in a universe without end or beginning and which passes through an infinite number of cosmic cycles. Each of these cycles is divided into phases of ascent and descent during which civilisations rise and fall.

One criticism I have is that a civilisation advanced enough to create universes would be advanced enough to leave a signature on their creation for their successors. To me, this seems to be an inevitable consequence of an advanced civilisation. Such a signature could take the form of, for example, a non-random pattern in the microwave background or a non-random clustering of galaxies. To date, no such signature has ever been identified.

John Byl of Trinity Western University, Canada, has discussed this proposal by Harrison, in a paper in the *Quarterly Journal of The Royal Astronomical Society*. First, he raises the problems, already discussed, of the untested and unknown theories concerning particle physics and singularities. Then he raises the objection that the process lacks evolutionary progress towards greater complexity. I think this is unjustified, since we have no evidence that evolution necessarily leads to increasing complexity. He then asks about the creation of the first universe adaptable to life. He postulates either the random or the theistic solution, without considering infinite regression. He concludes that the super-civilisation natural selection scenario is post hoc, unverifiable and reduces to an unnecessarily more elaborate version of the theistic or random principles, contravening Ockham's Razor. In fact, it could be verified by the discovery of a definite signature within our own universe, so it is verifiable but not verified.

There is the further possibility that the universe is not contingent at all. Perhaps some physical principle, as yet unknown, forces the physical constants to the values observed. Like the random theory, this still leaves the problem of the original formation. Why is there something instead of nothing?

A Prima Donna God

There is at least one overriding conclusion that can be deduced from the above conjectures. For the formation of life-forming galaxies, it is necessary that the values of the physical constants required be imposed, in some manner or other, upon the structure of the universe. This reminds us of Plato's concept of the pre-existence of matter. Any Creator, natural or supernatural, it would seem, is subject not only to the laws of mathematics but also to the constructs of physics. Of course, if the Supreme Being is really omnipotent and omniscient, then He could construct the universe in any manner He wishes. He could, like the God of the Bible, act in an arbitrary fashion, bringing triumph or disaster to his creatures at a whim. Hence the introduction of magic and superstition, with their accompanied cruelty and ignorance, to a large section of mankind. The idea of such a prima donna God is not, in my view, in accordance with the scientific evidence. The laws of physics do not change arbitrarily and no example of their contravention has yet been verified. Of course, it can be, and often is, argued that God is not constrained by mathematics, physical constructs, goodness, etc., etc., but that they are the reflection of God's nature (see *Beyond the Big Bang* by Drees). This seems to me to be equivalent. God is constrained by His nature.

Computer Immortality and the Omega Point

I will now attempt to discuss a book, already mentioned earlier in Chapter Three. Although written by a distinguished physics professor, I find it bizarre in the extreme. *The Physics of Immortality* by Frank Tippler, the Professor of Mathematical Physics at Tulane University in the USA. It is concerned with God, modern cosmology and the resurrection of the dead, all presented from a universal point of view. He purports to show that the central claims of Judaeo-Christian theology are true and are in fact straightforward deductions from the laws of physics. He uses for this demonstration a theory known as the 'Omega Point Theory', originally postulated by the Jesuit priest Pierre Teilhard de Chardin in his book *The Phenomenon of Man* (1955). De Chardin considers evolution to be divinely guided towards the Omega Point, which is defined as the end of history where the spiritual and material become one.

Tippler claims to make no appeal whatsoever to divine revelation, nor does he. He adopts a completely reductionist approach (all things can be reduced to the sum of their parts) and takes it to its logical conclusion in terms of computer technology.

Although he writes for the public, like most highly gifted mathematicians he greatly overestimates their scientific understanding. It is not easy to grasp Tippler's version of the Omega Point. It appears to be a point at the chronological end of the universe, a point at the end of time.

The first necessary condition for this theory is that the universe must be closed. From our discussion in Chapter Three, we find that such a universe will reach its maximum expansion and then start to collapse in on itself. As it collapses, its energy density will increase towards infinity. Defining life as 'information (thought) processing', the speed of this processing could increase correspondingly as the energy density increases. Since subjective time is experienced in terms of thought processes then life could extend infinitely. For this to occur, certain conditions must be fulfilled.

If the universe maintains isotropy, then it would collapse as a perfect sphere. The increase in temperature engendered by the collapse would eventually be fatal to any surviving life-forms. However, it is calculated that the isotropy of the universe could be made to decrease, causing the collapse to proceed at different rates in different directions. This gives rise to a temperature difference in different directions, which change an infinite number of times within the dilating time-scale. These temperature differences can supply sufficient free energy for the preservation of life. Furthermore, the reduction in size of the universe and the changing directions of collapse will allow all light signals to make contact throughout the whole of space-time. Eventually there will come a point in space-time where every part of the universe will be in the causal past of that point. This is what Tippler calls the Omega Point. An observer reaching this point would be able, with the right technology, to obtain information about everything that had ever happened in the universe. Life would be omniscient.

Tippler has introduced the Omega Point as the boundary condition that determines the structure of reality. Here the Omega Point determines a wave function that describes certain complex phenomena, one of which can be described as 'life'. The Omega Point determines this wave function and hence everything. In some respects, it represents the transcendence of God. Resurrection will occur by means of perfect simulation in infinite subjective time. This takes us a long way from observational cosmology yet it is based upon such observations. We have already mentioned the necessity for a closed universe. Hence, one of the observations necessary to confirm the Omega Point theory is that the amount of matter in the universe should be great enough to cause an eventual re-collapse of the universe to a singularity. The observations so far do not agree with this (see Coles and Ellis,

Chapter Five) although they may do so in the future. Tippler combines his theory with the many-worlds system of Everett. How the Omega Point can be compatible with such a theory is implicitly implied in his ideas on the resurrection.

This is an interesting theory but certain assumptions are made that cannot at the present time be verified. Possibly, some of them can never be verified. We have already discussed the assumption of a closed universe in Chapter Three. Another assumption is that life will spread throughout the universe as a result of advanced technology in the billions of years to come. This would be long after the earth has vanished from the scene. There is unfortunately no evidence that such would necessarily be the case. Various civilisations could reach a certain peak before being finally destroyed. We have on our own planet, the example of the Dark Ages that succeeded classical civilisation. It is also assumed that the increase in technology would be great enough to allow whatever life-form exists to manipulate space-time itself. Thus, it may be necessary to create the required anisotropy (unequal directional contractions) in the contracting universe to ensure the varying axes of contraction needed for the eternal continuation of life. The development of such technology would be a tall order, even for a very advanced civilisation.

Resurrection of the Dead by Emulation

Next, we come to the resurrection of the dead. For this feat, Tippler appeals to quantum mechanics. We have seen that a subatomic particle until observed is in a state of superposition. Once observed, a definite state is obtained. As we have seen, in Everett's 'Many Worlds' theory, all the states that we consider in superposition in fact exist as definite states in different universes. This also applies to human beings. We all exist in different states in different universes, but we are still the same person. Tippler enlarges on this to suppose that at the Omega Point, computer technology will be so advanced that an emulation of all people who have ever lived could be made in terms of their quantum state, and that in fact they would actually be the same person that had lived long ago. If you find this rather obscure, straining the bounds of credibility, I don't blame you. I find it rather baffling myself. If, for instance, it is possible to make such an advanced emulation of a person that had lived long ago, then surely a second identical emulation could be constructed. After that a third and a fourth and so on. Which one would be the original person?

The book is very long and contains much more in this vein, bringing in various scriptural ideas and quotes. In addition, it contains appendices of a highly technical nature for scientists.

The difficulty with the ideas and prognostications in this book is that, with the required assumptions, one can show that almost anything is possible. Just because the scenario is based upon physics and mathematics does not make it any more valid than one based upon intuitive mysticism, unless the assumptions made can be shown to be true, or at least highly probable. On the other hand, if the assumptions could solve some of the outstanding cosmological problems of the present day; that might be an indication of their validity. An example of this would be Alan Guth's assumption of an inflationary universe, previously discussed. As far as Tippler's book is concerned, neither the closure of the universe nor the assumption of continual technological progress, to the extraordinary extent postulated, fulfil these conditions.

Are We Perfectly Adaptable?

Another scientist who has written extensively about life in the universe is Freeman J Dyson. He claims to be optimistic about the future of the universe. In an open universe that expands forever, life will adapt to the lowering temperature. In a paper written for *Reviews of Modern Physics* entitled 'Time without End: Physics and biology in an open universe' he postulates two hypotheses with respect to life;

1   *The hypothesis of abstraction* which holds that the complexity of a life-form can be characterised by the amount of waste heat generated by some specific action. This can therefore be measured.

2   *The hypothesis of perfect adaptability*, given sufficient time life can adapt itself to any environment whatsoever provided that its temperature remains above the universal background temperature.

Under these conditions, Dyson calculates that the rate of metabolic energy falls with the square of the temperature. Hence taking into account hibernatory processes, life can survive for an infinite time on a finite amount of energy. The closed universe, he calculates, would be fatal to all life. Conversely, this is opposed to Tippler's speculation that a closed universe is necessary for life to survive infinitely in subjective time. Dyson's calculations do not take into account the conditions of an anisotropic collapse described previously. There is, moreover, a further condition necessary for the realisation of Dyson's speculations, that consciousness is dependent on structure rather than matter. This could be a problem for Dyson. In her book *The Human Brain* Susan Greenfield, a well-known expert on brain structure, writes:

'First and most obviously the brain is fundamentally a chemical system. Even the electricity it generates comes from chemicals. More significantly, beyond the fluxes of ions into and out of the neuron a wealth of chemical reactions are occurring incessantly in a bustling but closed world inside the cell. These events, some of which determine how the cell will respond to signals in the future do not have a direct electrical counterpart or any easy analogue with a computer.'

Such would make the brain, and hence consciousness, dependent on matter rather than structure. In the increasingly cold world of the future open universe, chemical reactions would become impossible, leading inevitably, to the final extinction of conscious life and eventually of all life. The heat death cannot be so easily surmounted.

Consciousness is the most mysterious phenomenon that we know of in the universe. Even if we could map every chemical reaction and every electrical impulse that the brain is capable of, we would still not know how external impulses from the physical world can be translated to the sights, sounds and feelings that we experience as individual conscious beings. We do know that without such reactions and impulses within the brain we could not survive. If it were possible to create an exact quantum copy of a brain and install it in some machine with the relevant attachments for the senses, would such a machine be conscious? Daniel Dennett in his book *Consciousness Explained* (it isn't) would answer 'yes'. It indeed appears that there is no evidence of any mysterious 'élan vital' in the brain's construction. Penrose, in *The Emperor's New Mind* and *Shadows of the Mind*, attempts to deal with this problem in terms of quantum indeterminacy. He appears to emphasise the electrical as opposed to the chemical functions of the brain and believes that we require some new law of physics to approach a complete understanding of this question. Hawking thinks, that Penrose has linked quantum theory with the workings of the mind because, since nobody really understands either, they must be connected in some way (see *The Large, the Small and the Human Mind*, Roger Penrose, p171). I personally can find nothing in the works of Penrose to justify this assertion. Such a connection may or may not be true but it is not obvious.

The Theological Argument

A very intellectual book written by Willem B Drees on the subject of cosmology and religion discusses the problem of religious belief within the concepts of modern cosmology and comes to the conclusion that 'the goodness of the world is affirmed by postulating God as the source of reality'. Unfortunately, since Drees is a Protestant theologian as well as a physicist, such conclusion is expected before one even starts the book. This is a pity because the book is very erudite. It investigates a whole gamut of scientific ideas and processes and their relationship to theology. It is, as Drees states himself, an apologetic study linking science and theology to make credible the existence of a God whose presence implies an ontological (the way the world is) harmony and unity between the realms of reality and spirituality. He writes:

'Theology can take up the language of science to express and develop the meaning of theological concepts. This helps communication about those concepts with people who feel at home in the scientific language. If ideas about God can be successfully embedded in a network of concepts, the ideas about God receive some credibility from the overall credibility of the network. If we can incorporate the best of contemporary cosmology, and thus much of physics and astronomy, the whole network then deserves to be taken seriously if the network is internally coherent.'

The first part of his book discusses the inconclusiveness of the arguments for the existence of a Creator or Designer God with respect to cosmology. The second part attempts to construct a theology in a scientific culture.

Chapter Four, the first chapter of part two, discusses eschatology. Eschatology is defined in the *Penguin English Dictionary* as: The study of ' "last things", death, judgement, heaven and hell'. Such a subject is obviously meat and drink to a theologian, especially one as talented as Willem Drees is. He considers two ways of understanding eschatology: as a theological reflection concerning the finiteness of existence or as a reflection concerning injustice. With respect to finiteness, we have a theological imaging of the future, either of individuals or the whole universe. It would reflect a desire for immortality. Such immortality is either objective (our contributions to the universe continue to exist) or subjective (implying the continuation of our own subjective feelings forever). With respect to injustice, we have a theological imaging of redemption and healing. Drees quotes Marjorie Suchocki, who considers that although belief in unending existence may well detract from an affirmation of the life in this world, we need subjective immortality to allow compensation for suffering and the overcoming of evil. Eschatology in this sense, it seems, will solve the Pandora problem (see Chapter Seven). The unfair suffering of the good will be compensated while the wicked shall be judged.

Drees then attempts to relate eschatology to science. First, he considers that science cannot explain or express moral values. Then he claims that some kind of metaphysical space with the possibility of unending existence might have a scientific formulation, like Tippler's Omega Point, discussed in the last chapter. Finally, he would seek an understanding of reality conforming to both science and the theological function of concern for justice and love. He considers the Bible valid concerning the underlying values of love and virtue. The method of expressing such value is much less important than the values themselves. Here he criticises both the fundamentalists and those who reject fundamentalism as being in thrall to the biblical images rather than fulfilling their capacity to express concern for justice and love. In this respect, he agrees with Rabbi Louis Jacobs whose book *We Have Reason to Believe* was discussed in Chapter Two.

In his discussion and criticism of both Tippler and Dyson, Drees values their contribution towards the scientific evaluation of theology, although he considers it rather overestimated, for reasons already given in the last chapter. He then discusses the concept of time looked at from a theological and corresponding cosmological point of view. He concedes that there are two ways of considering time. Firstly as a flow, whereby the actions of God in the universe itself can be implemented and understood. This corresponds to the scientific space-time of Big Bang cosmology. Secondly as a unity wherein all moments can be considered to exist simultaneously, encoding all possibilities at once in the quantum wave function of the universe. This would correspond to God's transcendence and timelessness, existing both within and without time. A view that was held by Boethius, Anselm and other important theologians of the past.

Drees concludes that pointing to methodological similarities between science and theology does not provide a method for linking them. He then introduces the idea of *constructive consonance* as a means of establishing such a relationship:

Consonance to give a desired coherence and harmony to the ideas,

Constructive because such harmony is a human construction.

His general assumptions are based upon three criteria (which are also assumptions):

1 Consistency

A theological position should possess internal consistency and be consistent with any science which it considers.

2 Meaning

The meaning of a theological position should be made clear or intelligible in terms of a scientific theory, since science itself is considered intelligible.

3 Relevance

The theological position must be relevant to our existence, both day to day and in the long term.

The credibility of the theology depends on the credibility and construction of the science used. The relevance of a theological or scientific theory from a pragmatic point of view could provide a reasonable ground for considering the theory true. I find this last assertion highly disputable. For example, a Ptolemaic universe is perfectly adequate for astro-navigation.

Drees attempts to construct a consonant God and a consonant world in the final chapter. He initially makes clear that any understanding of God remains revisable in a similar way to cosmology. He then looks at the location of God. This introduces the spatial metaphors of transcendence and immanence. He distinguishes four basic ideas regarding God's location with respect to the world.

1 Immanence

God and nature being thought of as co-existing leads to a form of pantheism

2 Temporal Transcendence: God as Creator

God as the Creator in a temporal sense postulates God as existing 'before' the universe. This leads to the paradox of God existing before He created 'time'.

3 Temporal Transcendence: God as the Eschaton. (The ultimate destiny.)

God understood as the one who completes and perfects the creation.

4 Spatial Transcendence

God conceived as a higher spatial dimensional reality. For instance our three-dimensional space could be embedded as a surface in a higher dimensional space with God at the centre, equidistant from all places. A more sophisticated version of 'the harmony of the spheres'.

Drees now summarises these four ideas in the term *present transcendence*. This emphasises the present as God's primary location but does not consider Him identical with the present. He is different from but intimately related to each present. The three functions of eschatology, judgement, appeal to action, and consolation, may be included in the understanding of God as present transcendence.

The process-theological view, developed based on the philosophies of Whitehead and Hartshorne, argues that there is no absolute beginning, but only an eternal process in which the universe and God exert influence on each other. God is both transcendent and immanent and is understood as the locus of values and possibilities. Drees adds a third component: God as the source of actuality.

Moral and aesthetic values are external to physics and cosmology, irrespective of whether they originated as a result of evolutionary natural selection or not. They are, however, internal to human beings. If we locate values in God then they are eternal, as God is eternal. Values that rely upon given situations are not real values but a disguise for opportunism.

As God is transcendent in space and time then all possibilities must be located in Him: the deterministic possibilities of classical physics, the superposition possibilities of quantum theory and the freewill possibilities of human action.

God as the source of actuality asserts that all reality is located in God. The creation of the universe, either temporal or eternal, is an expression of the mystery of existence. One can understand the universe as a gift of grace. God as the ground of actuality is a mystical complement of the two previous issues of values and possibilities.

The unity and diversity of God as a combination of the three aspects discussed above is reflected in the unity and diversity of the cosmos: the search for a complete unified theory of physics combining the electric, weak and strong forces with that of gravity, and the diversity in the studies of chaotic systems. In the Christian religion, God's unity is thought of as a trinity. God the Father, Creator of heaven and earth, parallels God as a source of actuality; Christ parallels God as a source of values and the Holy Spirit parallels God as the locus of possibilities.

The values and possibilities just introduced, which constitute the concept of God, are intended to effect the transformation of the world to greater conformity to the eternal values and to the goodness of its source.

The book contains an extensive set of appendices of the relevant scientific theories and ideas as well as an exposition of some of the religious literature with respect to cosmology.

The Faith of Religion and the Faith of Science

Beyond The Big Bang is a lucid and learned attempt to reconcile modern cosmology with religion. Its drawback lies in the fact that, as a Protestant theologian, the author is already committed to belief in God so his arguments are shaped by his conclusion. This tends to be the case with all committed apologists. However Drees is much more sophisticated than most, since his book is not written to persuade us to 'believe' but to show us that belief in God is not an unreasonable position to take, and that such belief can be constructed to take account of modern cosmology and other scientific ideas. As an ad-hoc argument, one can make a similar proposition for atheism or pantheism or any belief that does not directly contradict the scientific observations and experiments. Religious belief really comes down to a matter of faith. Faith is not only the ability to believe something for which there is no hard scientific evidence whatsoever, but also to go on believing it, even when all the evidence appears to point in the opposite direction. Proponents of religion consider it a matter of insight or intuition, similar in many ways to that invoked by some scientists for their discoveries, (e.g. Dirac, Poncaire, etc.). As Polkinghorne remarks: 'a leap not into the dark but into the light'. Sceptics consider it a matter of wishful thinking, of believing something because we desire it to be true, rather than because it is demonstrably true.

Science also relies on faith, but it is faith of a different kind. It is faith that the real world is reliably reflected and interpreted through the senses. As nobody can climb outside of his or her mind, we have no concrete evidence for this. As long as our interpretation is consistent and not self-contradictory, it appears to be a reasonable assumption. In addition to this, our survival in evolutionary terms would seem to rely upon our interpreting the real world, at least approximately, as it really is. The basic error of the three main Western Religions is the concept of humankind as the prime object of creation. Considering the extent of the universe, this is so unlikely, that it tends to invalidate all three of them, certainly from the eschatological and fundamentalist viewpoint. It does not necessarily invalidate their ethics, which are considered more fully in the final chapter.

Summary

Brandon Carter's 'Anthropic Principle' is considered. Some use this as an argument in favour of Deism. For example, Gerald Schroeder's book *Genesis and the Big Bang* argues from a scientific point of view not only the idea of Deism but also the literal truth of Genesis.

In his scientific papers and his book *The Life of the Cosmos*, Lee Smolin invokes a theory rejecting the existence of God. Smolin puts forward the theory that universes are made inside the event horizons of black holes, and therefore, the more stars and hence black holes, the more universes. Since stars are necessary for the formation of life, universes containing life will evolve by natural selection. This generalises Darwin's theory of evolution to the cosmos itself. The theory, together with criticisms by Rothman and Ellis, is examined in detail. Again, the problem of boundaries arises.

Edward Harrison's idea that our own life-forming universe was actually created by intelligent beings to ensure the indefinite continuation of life is examined, and various critical objections are put forward.

The arguments in favour of Deism are given scientifically by Tippler and Dyson, and philosophically in a lucid and concise manner by Willem Drees. His book *Beyond the Big Bang* is discussed in detail.

CHAPTER SEVEN

The Problem of Evil

WHY DID GOD MAKE GERMS?

The Pandora Problem

One of the main pillars of religion relates to the conduct of mankind. This has given rise to one of the knottiest problems of the three Western monotheistic religions: the problem of evil. I refer to this as the *Pandora Problem*.

According to Greek legend, Pandora was the first woman on earth. Zeus ordered Hephaestus, the lame artificer of the gods, to make her from clay. Each of the gods then conferred some gift upon her, hence her name, which means 'all-gifted'. Zeus sent Pandora to be the wife of Epimethius, the brother of Promethius, who had stolen fire from heaven to bestow upon mortals. The gods gave her a beautiful chest for safekeeping but told her that on no account should she open it. Evidently one of her gifts was curiosity, so of course she opened it, and out flew all the ills and troubles of the universe that have been with us ever since. Only the entity Hope remained to sustain mankind.

The evils that befall mankind can be divided into two types:

1   The evil that man practises upon man.

2   Suffering, the evil that befalls man through accident or disease, referred to in insurance documents as 'acts of God'.

Diseases were originally thought to be due to the wrath of God or Satanic influence. This was a logical deduction because the major religions are not only pre-Copernican, but also pre-bacterial.

Bacteria were first observed by Anton van Leeuwenhoek (1632–1723), the Dutch pioneer in microscopic observation. The subsequent work of Pasteur, Koch, Cohen and their associates, established the association of bacteria with specific diseases. Medical science now rests upon the basis that bacteria and viruses spread many diseases. It seems that, in most cases, the infliction of disease is a random event depending on how unlucky the victim is.

This presents certain problems for our mainstream Western Religions. Presumably, the Creator of the universe also created bacteria and viruses, many of them decidedly malignant. Why should God wish to inflict disease, in a random fashion, upon both animals and human beings? Indeed, in some instances, for example the Black Death, it looks as if God must have declared germ warfare on the human race. The question remains. Why did God make germs?

In general, how should we consider the evil arising through natural causes, a question so far unanswered by theologians? Many would include in this category the pain and distress of sentient animals through accident, disease, the natural action of predation and parasitism.

One example of a religion considering this would be Jainism, mentioned in the last chapter. Jainism, which arose in the sixth century BC in India, teaches respect for all living things. The Jainists believe in a cyclic universe and the transmigration of souls. They also believe in the Tirthankaras, the great Path-makers or teachers of Jainism, who guide their followers across the river of transmigration. Interestingly, they do not believe in a supreme Creator. Their overriding idea of right conduct is the practice of non-violence. To injure any living thing, even unwittingly, is a serious sin.

The first type of evil, that practised by man himself, is the one that seems to preoccupy most religions. The story of Adam and

Eve, in which Eve eats the forbidden fruit of the tree of knowledge, relates only to this first type of evil where man and woman fell from grace and were banished from paradise. On reflection, it does seem rather a drastic punishment for what was only a desire to satisfy a natural curiosity, a curiosity presumably implanted in Eve by the Creator. There is an interesting parallel with Pandora. However, Pandora's action covered both types of evil, hence the Pandora problem.

The Happy Sin

There is a school of thought among Christian theologians that classifies the sin of Eve as 'the happy sin'. This is because the expulsion from paradise, apart from necessitating Christ and the redemption, brought not only evil and suffering but instigated man's creativity. Without the expulsion, we would all have been running around paradise, immortal, happy but ignorant. There would have been no Plato, Confucius, Shakespeare, Michelangelo, Beethoven, Newton, Leonardo, etc., etc. Similar reasoning is applied to the Jewish concept of man's inclination to evil as well as to good, implanted in him by the Creator. Voltaire aptly expresses the idea in his tale of the Good Brahmin.

The Tale of the Good Brahmin

Voltaire writes that in his travels he met an old Brahmin, a very wise man of marked intellect and learning. Being rich, he lacked for nothing. Being wise, he needed to deceive nobody.

Near his exquisitely decorated house and garden, lived a narrow-minded old Indian woman who was both poor and a simpleton.

One day the Brahmin complained to Voltaire that he was thoroughly miserable because after forty years of study he realised even more acutely how ignorant he was. He could explain neither the presence of evil in the world nor how matter could produce thought. He did not know why he existed nor whether Brahma was borne of Vishnu or if they were both eternal. Every day people ask him questions on these points. He has to reply but has nothing worthwhile to say. He retires to his home stricken at his own curiosity and ignorance. Neither conversation with his companions nor study of the ancient texts allays his anguish. He is at times close to despair.

Voltaire became very worried about this good man's condition, especially since his unhappiness increased as his understanding developed and his insight grew.

That same day Voltaire met the old woman who lived nearby. He asked her if she had ever been troubled by the thought that she was ignorant of the nature of her soul She did not even understand the question. Never in all her life had she reflected for one moment on any of the mysteries that tormented the Brahmin. She believed devoutly in the metamorphoses of Vishnu and, provided she could obtain a little Ganges water with which to wash herself, she thought herself the happiest of women.

Struck with the happiness of this simple woman, Voltaire returned to the Brahmin and taxed him with his misery, when close by there lived an old simpleton who thought about nothing, and yet lives contentedly.

The Brahmin replied that he knew he would be happy if he were as brainless as his neighbour but would not care for happiness at the price of being a simpleton.

The Brahmin's answer impressed Voltaire so much that he put the matter before some philosophers. They all agreed that indeed they could be content with life were they simpletons but were not willing to trade reason for happiness.

I am not so sure myself that the choice of contentment versus reason is so clear-cut. Was the simpleton happy in a positive way or was she just 'not miserable'?

Before we discuss the various ways in which the problem of evil is confronted we should define the terms Deism and Theism.

Deism and Theism

Deism means the belief in a supreme being, a God that does not necessarily involve Himself in the day-to-day affairs of humanity: a God who could be responsible for the construction of the universe with all its special constants and conditions required for the existence of life. It is the Deity that most cosmologists would specify as sufficient and a few would specify as necessary. Aristotle believed in this kind of God. Aristotle's God is the Unmoved Mover, the ultimate cause of all things. The cosmos has emanated from Him as a necessary effect of His existence. He may not even be aware of the cosmos; He certainly has no effect whatever upon the world we live in. He cannot contemplate anything inferior to Himself and thus has no real religious relevance. However, He does activate the world by a process of attraction since the soul of man is drawn towards the purity of being. Man can become immortal and divine by purifying his intellect in contemplation of philosophical truth, together with the practice of the good life and concern for justice in society. A modern scientist could believe in this deity. In this case, the Pandora problem resolves itself into classifying evil as a psychological aberration caused by various environmental conditions combined with genetic influences. This is to be combated by social, psychological and medical responses. Natural accidents and tragedies cannot therefore be the result of divine retribution but are due to the very same laws of physics that ensure our existence. We can only try to ameliorate the results of such accidents using the best technology available. This kind of Deism does not necessarily imply the existence of an immortal soul. But it does implicitly regard the objectivity of truth, virtue and justice as attributes of the Godhead. Modified pantheism, the belief that God is the reality or principle behind nature, could easily be included in this kind of scientific Deism. Absolute pantheism, the belief that God actually is everything that exists is a belief totally incapable of any kind of verification, but then so are some cosmological speculations, for example the 'Many-Worlds' theory of Everett.

An example of a modified form of pantheism is the belief of Freeman J Dyson. He proposes the view that God Himself learns and grows as the universe unfolds and is therefore neither omniscient nor omnipotent. Dyson does not make any clear distinction between mind and God. God is what the mind becomes when it has passed beyond our comprehension. God could be a world soul or a collection of world souls of which we are the inlets on earth at the present stage of His development. We may later grow with Him as He grows or we may be left behind. The virtue of this theology is claimed to be the scope for diversity. The greatness of creation lies in its diversity, just like that of the Creator. Dyson claims this to be a heresy preached by Faustus Siconus in the sixteenth century, but I think this is an error. Siconus was an Arian who believed in the separateness of the Son from the Father and accepted neither the idea of redemption through Christ's sacrifice, nor the Trinity. He was one of the founders of Utilitarianism.

It was the German romantic philosopher Friedrich von Schelling (1775–1854) who postulated the concept of an evolutionary God.

Theism is the belief in a personal God who intervenes from time to time in the affairs of mankind. This is at the heart of all three Western monotheistic religions, Judaism Christianity and Islam As we have seen, these pre-Copernican religions have had their major assumption of the pre-eminence of mankind undermined by modern cosmology. In fact, a careful study of the liturgy, especially the Jewish liturgy, shows a solid foundation of primitive superstition. As the other two religions developed from Judaism this must also apply to them. There is indeed, a good case to be made that superstition is the foundation stone of all religions.

The Kabbalah

The Jewish Kabbalistic text, the Zohar, was written about 1275AD by the Spanish mystic, Moses of Leon. In it, the root of evil is found within God himself. In 'Din' or 'Stern Judgement', Din is depicted as God's left hand while Hesed (Mercy) becomes His right hand. As long as Din and Hesed operate harmoniously, the result is positive and beneficial. If Din breaks such harmony, it becomes evil and destructive. The Zohar does not tell us how the separation came about. The later Kabbalists reflected on the problem of evil and saw the result as a primordial accident in the very early stages of God's Self-revelation.

This idea of the dark side of God is reflected in the Jewish belief in the two sides of human nature as formed by God: the inclination for good and the inclination for evil that resides in all humankind. In the liturgy, there is much in praise of this God, for example.

'There is none to be compared unto Thee, neither is there any beside Thee, O Lord our God in this world, neither is there any beside Thee O our King, for the life of the world to come;' etc. etc.

This sort of praise one would normally think unnecessary for an omnipotent and omniscient God. He should know how wonderful he is, compared to us, without being told. The necessity for our abasement apparently comes from the primitive belief in the dark side of God. All this excessive and adulatory praise may at least limit the evil of Din, God's left hand. An effort which harks back far beyond the Kabbalists, to ancient superstition, when Jehovah was one of many competing deities, and sacrifice, perhaps even human sacrifice (the binding of Isaac) and superstitious ritual were used to placate this fierce god of the mountains. The fact that, in the process of time, Jehovah was transformed from the God of vengeance to the God of mercy can be put down to a form of wishful thinking. If we say how good and merciful God is then perhaps, He may become so. Never mention His dark side, pretend it does not exist, that is the safest way.

Such implicit superstition, engendered and invested by man's imagination, is the cornerstone of the three great monotheistic religions, but it has undergone many sophisticated developments over the ages. It has resulted in a proposed solution to the Pandora problem by a system known as dualism.

Dualism

Pure dualism consists of the belief in two supernatural powers, one of them good and the other evil. These two powers are equally strong and are in constant opposition. Which one will win this titanic struggle is unknown but at the end of time, one of them will be victorious. This belief gives a very neat solution to the Pandora problem.

Unfortunately, it is ethically neutral. If the outcome of this final conflict is unknown, then one can only be guided by self-interest, which, if taken to its logical conclusion, would lead to social chaos. In general, none of the mainstream religions promotes pure dualism. It is, however, believed or accepted by certain fringe cults such as Satanists who find the attraction of evil strongly bound up with various kinds of perverted sexuality.

The religion with beliefs closest to pure dualism is Zoroastrianism. It is a somewhat modified form of dualism, since ethical neutrality would undermine the whole idea or basis of a religion. The history of this religion dates back to about 3000BC when there were large-scale migrations of people from Eastern Europe into Western Europe, including the geographical areas we now know as Greece, Italy and Scandinavia. There was a similar migration eastwards through Persia into India where they conquered the Indus Valley civilisation. In about 1500BC, a second wave migrated to Persia. The groups migrating into India and Persia referred to themselves as Aryans, which means 'the noble ones'.

Theirs was a primitive religion of natural forces. Like the ancient Israelites, they did not think of their gods in human form. They thought of them as abstract concepts such as Truth and Victory. Their demons likewise took such forms as Wrath, Greed and Cruelty. Paradise after death was only for the priests and kings.

Zoroaster himself was probably the first of the world's great religious prophets. He appeared in Persia about 1200BC when the country was just emerging from the Stone Age. He was a priest who was married with several children. When he was about thirty years of age, he experienced a series of visions, which inspired him to preach a new message. It took many years of preaching before a local king called Vishtasp was persuaded to adopt his teaching as the official religion of his small kingdom. This religion in time spread throughout Persia and finally became the mainstay religion of the great Persian Empire.

The chief tenet of Zoroaster's teaching is that of one's personal responsibility to choose freely between good and evil. On this choice alone will it depend how a person is judged in the hereafter. The social status of the individual will have no bearing upon this judgement. Those who, on balance, are considered good will go to heaven; the others will go to hell. This teaching offended the established priests and elite of society who had previously regarded paradise as theirs alone, an exclusive club to keep out the common people.

Zoroaster taught that God is wholly good. He is the Creator of all things good, the physical and spiritual worlds of humanity and the heavens. He is called Ahura Mazda and is the friend of all mankind. The evil in the world emanates from the Destructive Spirit Angra Mainyu who is the dark god of cruelty and violence. He created the evil demons. He rules in hell and has been an enemy of God from the beginning of time. In no way can he be described like Satan as a fallen angel. God cannot be the Creator of evil. Such an idea would be anathema to the Zoroastrians. The world is the battlefield of the forces of good and evil. Mankind was made by God to assist Him in this battle.

God also created spiritual beings called Amesha Spentas (Bounteous Immortals). Corresponding in some ways to the Christian archangels but more abstract in conception, they are Righteousness, Dominion, Devotion, Immortality and Wholeness. They also represent the virtues to which we should all aspire if we are to share in God's Kingdom. According to Zoroaster, the world is essentially good but it is corrupted by evil. In the final days, the forces of God will be triumphant, evil will be destroyed and the world restored to perfection. The dead will be raised to judgement. The righteous will dwell with God and the wicked languish in hell. In Zoroastrianism, hell is not eternal. Its purpose is corrective. Finally, after punishment and repentance, even the most wicked will return to God, who will reign supreme over the world.

In this case, pure dualism is given a twist. The dice are loaded in favour of God. In the final analysis, God will win out. All the same, it is the nearest religion to pure dualism that we know of, evil and good being two entirely separate spiritual forces.

That this religion bears many similarities to Christianity is not surprising. By the time Jesus was spreading his Christian message, Zoroastrianism, as practised by the Persian Parthians, was the most powerful religion in the known world. Zoroastrianism is still practised today by the Parsis in modern India. They number only about 70,000 and live mainly in Bombay.

In Christianity and Judaism dualism, although still ostensibly a basis for the solution of the Pandora problem, became much more complicated than for the Zoroastrians. The problem of evil was compounded by the problem of the unity of the Godhead. The Jews had always had difficulty in ascribing the evil inherent in the universe to God when God Himself was looked upon as their special protector and guardian. Indeed, from the Nevi'im (prophets), Isaiah 45: 7 God explicitly states:

'I form the light and create darkness: I make peace and create evil: I the Lord do all these things.'

The basic Orthodox assumption, that any suffering inflicted was due to the sins and wickedness of the people, was destroyed for Progressive Judaism by the holocaust. Of what sin could children of less than five years be guilty, for a million of them to be murdered in the gas chambers of the Third Reich? Progressive Jews who found the Kabbalistic interpretation regarding the separation of Din, the left hand of God, somewhat esoteric, adopted an approach similar to that of Spinoza. God's vision incorporates what appears to us as evil, as part of the divine plan. In essence, all will be seen to be the necessary prelude to the Messianic age when every knee will bend to the ultimate ruler of the universe. In other words, we do not have a solution to the Pandora problem but God has, and in His own good time, all will be revealed. Thus, dualism is a purely local phenomenon. In the long term, it is illusory, for we cannot see God's overall view.

In the Christian and Muslim religions, dualism is crystallised in the form of the Devil, Satan and his demons. Originally, in the Torah, Satan is described as ha-satan the 'Adversary'. This is not an office denoting wickedness but one most beloved of God. There seems to be no concept of good and evil angels in the Torah but only of heavenly messengers. However, by the time the New Testament was compiled, Satan has become a fallen angel who, with his legions of lesser angels rebels against God and is cast out of heaven into hell. Like Angra Mainyu in Zoroastrianism, he embodies the spirit of rebellious destruction and is responsible for all the evil in the world. In this way, the Pandora problem is solved. Unlike the Zoroastrian belief, Satan was originally created by God, which brings a contradiction into the idea of an omnipotent and omniscient God. If God is omniscient, he must have known of the heavenly rebellion and if he is omnipotent why did he not stop it? These questions have never been answered satisfactorily. The usual answers involves statements such as: 'it is all part of God's overall plan', or: 'it's one of God's mysteries'. It is a question that has spawned endless Christian and Muslim heresies regarding the nature of God. The Devil is an essential ingredient of any religion that preaches redemption. Even the Protestant reformer, Martin Luther, said that without the Devil and the threat of damnation there is little need either for Christ or His Church. Evidently, Satan had many allies and legions. Ammael, Araquiel, Araziel, Asael, Asbeel, Azael, Azza, Baraqijal, Exael, Ezeqeel, Gadreel, Kasdaye,

Kashdejan, Kokabel, Penemuel, Penemue, Pharmoros, Satanail, Talmaiel, Tamiel, Turel, Usiel, to name but a few. There were many others, numbered in their hundreds of thousands. They were seen as fearsome demons with talons and pointed teeth, corresponding indeed to the evil forces released by Pandora. Thus was the universe in the Middle Ages interlinked with the abode of both God and Satan. The universal confrontation of God and his heavenly host of angels against Satan and his dark legions intruded and overshadowed the physical world of science and empiricism.

Summary

The main concern of this chapter is how the various religions deal with the concept of evil in its different forms. This is referred to as the Pandora problem, from the legend of Pandora in Greek mythology.

The God of Aristotle is described as being the God that a religious scientist could believe in. The concept of pantheism is introduced and Freeman Dyson postulates the idea of a God evolving with the universe, an idea originally conceived by the romantic philosopher Schelling.

The development of religion from superstition is considered with reference to the Kabbalah of Judaism. The most usual solution to the problem of evil is to be found in some form of dualism (the equal and opposing forces of good and evil). The closest religion to pure dualism, Zoroastrianism, is examined in detail.

The Christian and Moslem idea of the Devil or Satan as the focus of evil is shown to be a modified form of dualism and involves conflict as an essential part of the universe.

CHAPTER EIGHT

Consciousness

WHAT MAKES BRAINS THINK?

Before we dismiss such dualistic ideas entirely, as the fevered imaginings of mediaeval society, let us return to the 'Many Worlds' theory of Everett described in Chapter Five. Everett considered the idea of parallel universes corresponding to the collapse of every quantum wave function. Could it be possible for a parallel universe to co-exist linked not by the quantum wave function but by the phenomenon of consciousness? At present, there appear to be at least four things inimical to scientific understanding: Space-time singularities, quantum superposition, the origin of life-forms, and consciousness.

We saw in Chapter Six that consciousness is a very strange facet of the physical universe. The universe would be easier to understand and much more coherent without the development of life-forms and consciousness. The universal history would follow a logical process of the effects of the electrical, gravitational, strong and weak forces. Physical and chemical reactions would shape the galaxies, stars and planets, which would form, burn and die throughout the aeons. Unfortunately, we would not be here to understand it. We know that consciousness is linked to chemical and electrical reactions within the brain but nobody understands how such reactions could give rise to the thoughts, emotions and desires of the higher mammals and the sense of identity experienced by individual human beings. Paul Davies, in his book *Are We Alone?* mentions the law of self-organisation that was discussed in Chapter Two with respect to the origin of life. He considers that in some deep and mysterious way the same process could be responsible for the origin of consciousness. Could there be a cosmological basis for these phenomena?

A Cosmological Basis for Consciousness

So far, we have considered other universes that may exist in series or in parallel with our own. Although many of them would be strange and weird places with different fundamental constants relating to their structure, they would still possess such constants; for example, the gravitational constant or the speed of light. Consider a universe with a structure so different that none of these constants exists. There would be no such domain as particle physics as we know it, no such thing as light or gravity or electricity or anything else that we could comprehend. Is such a universe possible? I can think of no overwhelming reason to rule it out. But is there any way in which we could be made aware of it? If this strange universe were to run parallel to our own, then one of the points of contact could be through our minds or, indeed, through the minds of all conscious creatures throughout our universe. In other words, the intersection of the two universes would be conscious minds. This is not to be considered a miraculous construction but an extension of physics. Do we have any evidence of this intersection? In general, the mystics and the devout would say yes, while most scientists would say no.

This idea of a strange parallel universe where the normal laws of physics no longer exist is not a new idea. It has been expressed in myth and legend through the ages. The Norse Valhalla, the Greek realm of Hades, the Christian heaven, all these express in some way the existence of some 'other-worldly' construct sometimes made known to us through meditation or dreams or visions but always through the mind. Many writers have used the idea of a distant land or country where very strange happenings occur. Sometimes these lands are part of our own world but with peculiar properties. For instance, James Milton's *The Lost Horizon* where people in the valley of Shangri-La can live forever, or the strange worlds of Mars and Venus conjured up by C S Lewis in his 'science fiction' novels. In fact, they are really science fantasy, used to propagate the ideas of Christianity. In his Narnia stories, Lewis introduces a parallel universe that can be entered via a wardrobe – a very entertaining set of stories ostensibly for children but really bringing Christian ideas to readers of all ages. The mystical formulation of a strange and unknown universe is the foundation of the supernatural. Is there, or could there be, any real scientific evidence available in our own universe, for the existence of the supernatural in the form of a parallel universe? If the structure of such a parallel universe were completely alien to any structure of our known universe, then scientific investigation in respect of the laws of physics would seem a hopeless task. There is, however, one branch of science that may throw some light on the possible existence or not of this postulated universe. That is the science of neurology. If the link between our universe and its *un-physical* parallel is the consciousness that is present throughout the whole universe, then the study of the physical link between mind and brain would be the obvious place to start.

As my own discipline is observational cosmology and not neurology, I shall attempt to examine this subject from the cosmological viewpoint of parallel universes rather than the physiology of the brain. But some knowledge of the make-up of the brain is necessary if any evidence is to be discovered, and hence my extensive use of books by Ramachandran and Blakeslee, Steven Rose and others whose works are referenced in the bibliography. I have also used Roger Penrose's latest book, *Shadows of the Mind* in which Penrose has referenced S R Hameroff, B Libet and others for his chapter on 'Quantum Theory and the Brain'. The Internet has also been a useful source of information, with papers by Chalmers, Dennett, Beloff, King and many others.

Elementary Brain Structure

The brain has not always been associated with mental activity.

The Egyptians of the Middle Kingdom (2040BC to 1786BC) did not even preserve the brain with the rest of the body, the heart, lungs and liver being considered far more important.

The ancient Greeks thought that the brain was the site of the soul or spirit and that all thoughts and emotions were centred on the heart. The great Greek physician Hippocrates (460BC to 377BC), the father of medicine, gradually undermined these ideas. He based his work upon experience, observation and reason. His thought passed to the School of Alexandria where Herophilus and Erasistratus by dissection, traced connections (nerves) leading from the rest of the body into the brain. This, combined with the discovery by Alcmaeon of Croton, of connections between the eyes and the brain led to the concept of the brain as the seat of thought.

Galen (129BC to AD199), a Greek physician in Roman times, concluded from the observation of wounded gladiators that the brain was the organ of sensation and bodily movement.

In spite of these advances in the ancient world, the debate over the brain versus the heart, as the source of thought and emotion, continued into the Middle Ages and beyond.

The brain is an extremely complicated organ. The terminology used to describe it is equally complicated. In this chapter, a somewhat simplified description is given in an attempt to offer at least some understanding of the problem of consciousness.

The average human brain weighs about three pounds and divides into left and right cerebral hemispheres. These enclose most of the other sub-cortical parts. The amygdala, the hypothalamus, the hippocampus, the medulla, the cerebellum, the pons, the raphe nuclei, the locus coeruleus, the reticular system and the pituitary and pineal glands. The two cerebral hemispheres are connected by the corpus callosum that relays information between them. The brains of other mammals have a similar if simpler, construction.

Below is a table of some of the main brain functions. In fact, all parts of the brain are interconnected in a very complicated way so the following table is only a very elementary and restricted overview.

Cerebral Cortices (Hemispheres)	The site of advanced mental abilities and movement
Thalamus	Transmits auditory and visual signals to cortex and Amygdala
Amygdala	Responds emotionally to external objects
Hippocampus	The layout of places and routes between them (Cognitive Maps)
Reticular System	Wakefulness
Raphe Nuclei	Sleep
Pons and Locus Coeruleus	Modulates the Reticular System and Raphe Nuclei
Cerebellum	Helps co-ordinate movements
Medulla	Controls Blood Pressure, Heart Rate, Breathing, etc.
Hypothalamus	Metabolism, Hormones, Aggression, Fear, Sexuality, etc.
Pituitary Gland	Conducts the hormonal signals from the Hypothalamus to the body
Pineal Gland	Regulates the sleep cycle, secretes Melatonin

TABLE THREE: BRAIN FUNCTIONS

Table Three should be examined in conjunction with Diagram Four.

The two cerebral hemispheres are the largest feature of human and other primate brains. Each hemisphere receives information from the opposite side of the body, which in general it controls. They can act together because they share information relayed through the corpus callosum. They are also indirectly connected through their sub cortical structures. Each hemisphere is divided into four lobes separated by fissures. The lobes themselves are

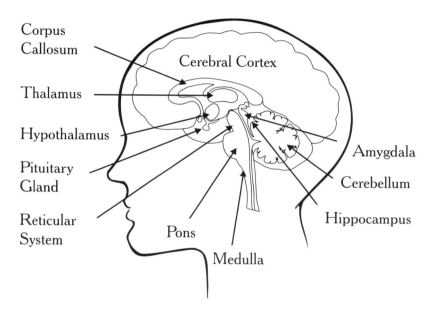

Corpus
Callosum

Cerebral Cortex

Thalamus

Hypothalamus

Pituitary
Gland

Reticular
System

Pons

Medulla

Amygdala

Cerebellum

Hippocampus

DIAGRAM FOUR

A simplified diagram of the human brain

divided into different areas defined by the stimuli that activate their cells and by the defective behaviour caused when they are damaged. The identification of many of the areas is still a topic of research.

The brain structure itself is composed of two general types of specialised cells: nerve cells (neurons) and glial cells (glia). The glia support and protect the neurons. There are about a hundred billion neurons in the human brain and about the same amount of glia. Neurons have many different characteristic shapes but in general consist of a cell body (soma) with a number of fibrous branches called the dendrites. It also has one fibre, the axon. The soma contains the chemical organisation for synthesising essential molecules. The dendrites and the soma are the areas of signal input while the axon is the transmitter. Messages are sent via the dendrites and axons of neighbouring neurons to distant and/or local parts of the brain. Information is conveyed from the axon of one neuron through the dendrites of another by means of tiny gaps called synapses. Each neuron can have as many as 100,000 synapses. The brain can thus receive and transmit the enormously complicated transactions necessary for a conscious life-form to survive. Communication within the brain depends upon both electrical and chemical signals. The neuron-generated signal consists of an electrical impulse carried along its axon by charged ions of potassium and sodium. It is transmitted chemically across the synapses. The chemical molecules used in the transmission are known as neurotransmitters, of which there are as many as fifty different types. In addition to neuron-neuron transmission, there is neuron-glia and glia-glia transmission. The unsolved problem of consciousness is how these electrical and chemical signals can give rise to a thinking conscious creature, which also has a sense of self-identity, and in humans, at least, a sense of its own consciousness.

According to the philosopher and mathematician René Descartes (1596–1650), human beings consist of minds and bodies. The mind, for him, is spiritual and lacking extension, although he does write

René Descartes

of the soul having a general influence throughout the body. He suggests that it is in the brain, and more specifically in the pineal gland, that it exercises its functions more particularly than in all the others. He gives no evidence for this, and it is now known that the pineal gland regulates the body's rhythms in response to the daily cycle of light and darkness. Descartes also writes that the soul is not just lodged in the body like a pilot in a ship but is intimately conjoined with it. He claims that therefore mind and body form a certain unity. This theory is known as 'dualism', not to be confused with the religious dualism discussed in the last chapter.

The idea of a ghostly mind conjoined with the brain and governing our actions and thoughts is no longer considered acceptable by most neurologists. Dennett disparagingly refers to the mind's Cartesian Theatre. In this, he is referring to some place within the brain where all the inputs and sensations are put together to form conscious thought and action. He labels this as 'Cartesian Materialism'. In fact, a network of brainstem structures, the reticular formation, the pons, the raphe nuclei and the locus coeruleus control wakeful consciousness. The nearest thing to the 'Cartesian Theatre' of Dennett seems to be an area of the frontal cortex designated as Area 46. At the moment, this is the best candidate for the role of the brain's central executive. It seems to be co-ordinator of thoughts and task-switching, but the content of consciousness depends on which areas of the cortical hemispheres are operational at the time. Since there is an Area 46 in each of the frontal hemispheres, a person who has had their corpus callosum severed can appear, in theory, to possess a double-consciousness or personality. This is the basis of Robert Louis Stevenson's famous story of Dr Jekyll and Mr Hyde. Whether such cases have ever existed in practice is highly questionable. Ramachandran has so far been unable to find a clear-cut case of dual-personality disorder. When he telephoned friends in psychiatry asking for the names of patients with personality disorder, he was informed that they had seen such patients, but they had several personalities rather than just two. One had nineteen 'alters' inside him. Such claims, that appear to be gilding the lily, make Ramachandran deeply suspicious of the whole phenomenon. He claims that dual personality defies common sense, since two personalities inhabiting one body appears to be impossible. He puts forward the theory of diametrically conflicting beliefs causing unbearable stress, whereupon the person involved seals these beliefs from each other, causing the apparent effect of dual personality. Such stress could be caused by physical or sexual childhood abuse. In this case, it would seem that each of the cortical Areas 46 would be acting in such a way as to be independent of each other. Unfortunately dual, or multiple personality disorder (MPD), continues to be largely ignored by the medical community, possibly due to the lack of any specific accredited cases.

Consciousness Unexplained!

From what we have discussed so far, it is obvious that the neuronal electrical and chemical reactions within the brain are an absolute pre-requisite for the phenomenon of consciousness.

So far, this is all that has been established, in spite of the fact that the research papers published each year run into hundreds of thousands. The difficult problem of converting the physics of the brain into thought and action is still a matter of fierce debate.

One school of thought is that the laws of physics can indeed explain consciousness: the complicated workings of neuronal activity within the brain form an algorithm of stunning complexity which not only gives rise to but is itself conscious activity. This viewpoint, popular among scientists working with computer-designed artificial intelligence, is termed functionalism and is championed very eruditely by the philosopher Daniel Dennett. John Searle, in his book *The Mystery of Consciousness* claims that Dennett in his book *Consciousness Explained* denies the existence of consciousness. I think that this is rather unfair. Firstly, you cannot explain something that does not exist. Secondly, you cannot explain something unless you understand it. Dennett appears to equate consciousness with understanding rather than with subjective feelings such as pain, colour and discrimination. Understanding can result from an algorithmic response to brain stimulation and can in principle be investigated scientifically through neurological research. Dennett considers that the subjective feelings of the kind mentioned above are private to each individual and are thus rendered impervious to objective scientific investigation. To all intents and purposes, therefore, they might just as well not exist and in fact are just side-effects of the algorithmic response mechanism in the brain.

This point of view has its own problems. At what stage of complexity does a computer or a brain activate understanding? According to Dennett, it is at the stage of 'demons in the software'. By this, he means a host of subprograms dealing with fiction, second intention, language, etc. But why should subprograms rather than main programs indicate the crossover level?

A similar problem arises with respect to the formation of consciousness in the foetus. Somewhere there must be this magic changeover point, unless one adopts the pansychic principle that everything in the universe has some potential form of consciousness, including the various parts of your own body. This algorithmic changeover point sounds a bit like one of Dennett's skyhooks. In fact, Dennett could be said to be hoist by his own skyhook. A computer works on arithmetic to the base two. The electric current within its circuit indicate one when on and zero when off. It is therefore only an abacus with one bead per row. No one but a pansychic would dream of attributing consciousness to an abacus or even a complicated interrelated system of abaci that in principle can represent any computer program you care to name. A computer, however, is an electronic abacus. Could it be the electricity, which at a certain level of algorithmic complexity generates the consciousness of artificial intelligence? How many pulses of electric current does it take to generate consciousness? If electricity is indeed the basis of consciousness then this leads back to the pansychic principle mentioned above, since all material substances are formed from charged particles, protons, electrons, etc.

In addition, there is the problem of brain chemistry. Here indeed is a dualism accepted unquestionably by all neurologists: the dualism of chemistry and electricity. The chemistry gives rise to neuronal transmissions of electricity, which in turn affects the chemistry not only of the brain, but of other parts of the nervous system as well; a virtuous circle of brain activity leading to both conscious and unconscious effects. To simulate the brain's activity and consciousness for strong artificial intelligence (strong AI) would require, it seems, the construction of both chemical and electrical reactions. Such a simulation, if possible, would no longer be an artificial brain but a real one. Even if such a construct were made in the laboratory, we would be no nearer to solving the problem of consciousness unless in the construction we found the magic crossover point from the unconscious to the conscious. That consciousness or understanding is therefore an emergent property, i.e. a property equal to more than the sum of its parts (see *On the Moral Nature of the Universe*, Murphy and Ellis, p24), is evident even to materialists like Dennett. The question is, how does it emerge?

The Theorem of Godel

An opposing school of thought is that of the mathematician Roger Penrose mentioned in Chapter Four. He considers that the brain is not algorithmically based. To verify this statement, he uses a theorem of Godel. 'No formal system of sound mathematical rules of proof can ever suffice to establish all the true propositions of ordinary arithmetic.'

This established that human understanding and insight could not be reduced to a set of computational rules or algorithms. Dennett would counter this by claiming that understanding and insight themselves could be the result of yet unknown algorithms and that Godel's theorem is not relevant to the workings of the mind. Be that as it may, Penrose goes on to consider the quantum effects within the brain in the light of Godel's theorem. First, he considers the structure of the neurons. Each neuron has its own complicated control system known as the cytoskeleton that also holds the cell in shape. This structure consists of protein molecules, actin, microtubules and intermediate filaments, arranged in various ways. He then goes on to describe the microtubules, hollow cylindrical tubes of the order of one millionth of a millimetre in diameter and with lengths of the order of a millimetre. They can grow or shrink as required and transport neurotransmitter molecules. They form communicating networks along the dendrites and the axons, each microtubule communicating with the next one by means of microtubule-associated proteins. They are responsible for maintaining the strength of the synapses and for effecting alterations of these strengths when necessary. They also organise the growth of new nerve endings and guide their connections towards other nerve cells. It seems that they play an important part in the brain's plasticity where the interconnections are continually undergoing subtle changes. Penrose claims that as it is the microtubules that seem to control the brain there must be something within the microtubules that is different from computability. He argues that such non-computational activity must be the result of some large-scale quantum-coherent phenomenon coupled to macroscopic behaviour. Quantum coherence occurs when large numbers of particles co-operate in a single quantum state unentangled with the environment. Such coherence is necessary because single random quantum effects would be lost within the macroscopic structure.

In general, quantum coherence is observed in such phenomena as superconductivity, where electrical resistance drops, and superfluidity, where a fluid's viscosity drops, in both cases to zero. This will occur only when the surrounding environment has a very low temperature without enough energy to become entangled with the relevant quantum state. For quantum coherence to take place within a biological system with a relatively high temperature, the

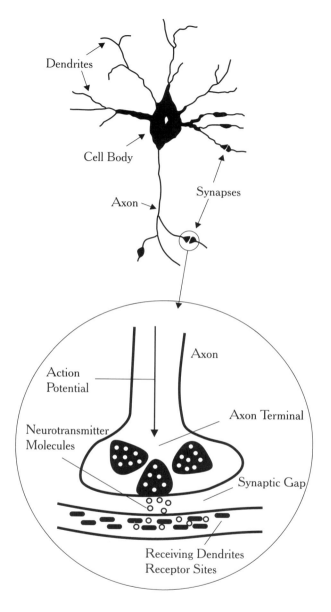

Dendrites

Cell Body

Axon

Synapses

Action
Potential

Axon

Neurotransmitter
Molecules

Axon Terminal

Synaptic Gap

Receiving Dendrites
Receptor Sites

DIAGRAM FIVE

*The electrical and chemical reactions
within the brain*

energy gap necessary between the environment and the particles must result from a very high rate of metabolic drive. There is, Penrose states, some respectable observational evidence for this in many biological systems.

Evidence that the cytoskeleton is related to consciousness is provided by the action of the many different chemicals that can be used as anaesthetics for the brain. Since these chemicals are so different, it is not the chemistry that is responsible for the anaesthesia but the electric dipole moments that interrupt the functioning of the microtubules. It appears that consciousness could be caused by some non-computational physical action that is incorporated within the activity of the microtubules. Since we have seen that the nature of consciousness is a result of many parts of the brain acting simultaneously, then the required physical action must affect many millions of cytoskeletons with their microtubules and their connections. If this is the result of large-scale quantum coherence as suggested by the distinguished physicist Herbert Frohlich, then it would be an amazing feat for nature to achieve by biological means. Penrose thinks that such a feat is evident by the fact of our own mentality. To some extent, this is a more sophisticated concept of Dennett's idea of the increased complexity of the software. Unfortunately, this is where Penrose comes to an abrupt halt. How the result of such biological action transfers into consciousness he ascribes to a principle of physics as yet unknown. In his book *Shadows of the Mind*, he gives a very lucid and much more detailed account of the search for the missing science of consciousness, although some of the mathematics may be daunting for the lay reader. Like every other researcher, he does not really know the answer but he has certainly pioneered a practical and logically consistent method of investigation.

The Parallel Universe

Let us now return to the idea of a non-physical parallel universe running in concert with our own. Consider such a universe as being a source of conscious thought, intelligence and self-organisation. Also, consider that such a universe is a source of conflict. What kind of conflict we don't know, but a conflict that could have some possible bearing on the religious myths and beliefs described in the last chapter.

We certainly know that our own universe is a source of conflict both local and global. In fact the whole idea of evolution through natural selection depends on the survival of those life-forms best able to win conflicts, both with the environment and with other life-forms. In fact, a good atheistic or anti-religious argument can be made on the basis of the enormous amount of suffering and pain among sentient creatures that was necessary to produce mankind through evolution. Could this be the work of a merciful and loving God?

If the intersection of a non-physical, conscious and intelligent universe with our own is through the consciousness of sentient beings, then one would expect any sense of conflict to be reproduced in our own universe. This in no way proves that such a non-physical universe exists but is an expected consequence if it does. Thus the moral idea of the conflict of good and evil could have a cosmological basis. We have here the idea of a dualism in respect of consciousness; not the individual dualism so decried by modern biologists but a form of universal dualism, wherein, a parallel universe to evolve life and consciousness underpins certain forms of chemical and electrical reaction. This could perhaps be the basis of functionalism and the self-organisation phenomenon investigated and described by Stuart Kauffman and Co. It sounds suspiciously like the 'life force' postulated by the philosopher Bergson. Unlike his philosophy, a non-physical parallel universe would inform matter with consciousness. It would not be in conflict with it. The conflict in our universe would have a much deeper source within the non-physical universe, a source about which we can only speculate since, like the interior of black holes it does not seem to be amenable to scientific investigation. Speculating further, our universe could indeed be the emanation of a non-physical parallel universe through some form of tunnelling process resulting in a quantum generated 'Big Bang'.

Tests for a Parallel Universe

Is there any way in which we can test such a theory? After all, this idea is no more speculative than Everett's system of a vast number of parallel physical universes, which is considered possibly viable by such renowned physicists as Steven Weinberg, Stephen Hawking and Murray Gell-Mann among others. It is no more speculative than the processes posited by Smolin and Harrison, that may or may not lead to other universes in the interior of black holes. True, we have evidence of quantum superposition and the collapse of the wave function with observation that leads to the idea of the 'Many Worlds' theory. We also have evidence of the probable existence of black holes leading to the multi-universe theory. However, we have the incontrovertible evidence of consciousness manifesting itself in the form of non-conscious matter and energy, which leads to the non-physical parallel universe theory.

One way to test for this theory is to look for evidence of the supernatural or paranormal. Unfortunately, this area of inquiry is beset with frauds and charlatans, with metal benders, astrologers, mediums, fortune-tellers, etc. Very few respectable scientists are prepared to accept any connection whatever with such a project. Firstly, most evidence presented is anecdotal and such evidence in general is not scientifically acceptable. Secondly, we have extrapolation from the beliefs and customs of mankind throughout the ages of some kind of supernatural domain. This is even less acceptable than anecdotes. As we have seen, men believed for many thousands of years that their abode on this earth was the centre of the universe. This did not make it objectively true. The only scientifically acceptable evidence is statistical or experimental. The problem is that a scientist can be fooled just as easily as anyone else by a skilled magician, and some have been made into laughing stocks through their own arrogant assumption that their skills of observation would allow them to detect any fakery.

To quote from Stephen Jay Gould's book, *An Urchin in the Storm*, ' "Extra Sensory Perception" is not impossible *a priori* but who wants to invest precious years of a career in an area so rife with fakery not easily detected by the ordinary methods of science? Thus, ironically, the fools and frauds are keeping their own ship from a potential port.'

Suppose for the sake of argument that the validity of some form of paranormal phenomenon could be demonstrated. Does this imply the existence of a non-physical parallel universe? It would certainly be a lead in that direction. Whether it would also imply the existence of God is more doubtful. It might imply the existence of some kind of intelligence causing an emanation of the physical universe in the 'Big Bang' with all the conditions and constants tuned to produce life and hence consciousness. What this intelligence could be is an open question. Could this parallel universe be the source of some of the abstract archetypes postulated by Plato? Could it also be the source of mathematics? If we assume that the intersection of the physical and non-physical universe is through consciousness, then the answer could be 'yes' to both questions. With respect to our universe, no form of guidance or divine interference would be necessary to produce the required consciousness and intelligence once the right conditions and constants had been set in motion. Although evolution is not necessarily progressive, it would certainly be so on some planets in a vast universe. This would follow from the 'normal distribution':

The Normal Distribution

The 'normal distribution' is formed by plotting a graph of quantity against some quality inherent in a sample of objects. It forms a bell-shaped curve, showing that there are a few objects of very low quality, with the largest number of objects having a medium

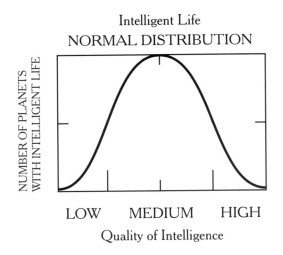

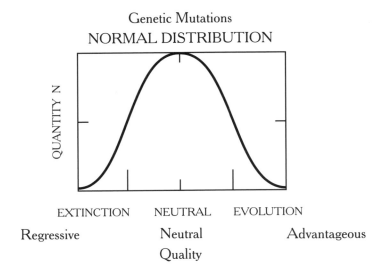

DIAGRAM SIX

Normal distribution of intelligent life; normal distribution of genetic mutations.

quality, and again with a few objects of very high quality. This distribution is ubiquitous throughout the universe, hence its name. The vast majority of objects, when sampled in this way, follow the normal distribution to a lesser or greater extent. The reason for this is not obvious from the cosmological point of view. It seems to be one of the conditions of the universe (see Diagrams 6).

It is reasonable to assume, therefore, that the evolution of intelligence on planets that bear conscious intelligent life would follow the normal distribution.

The normal distribution could also be a necessary condition for the evolution of life-forms. Genetic mutations are the reason why we are not all carbon copies of each other. If we plot the number of genetic mutations affecting a species in a given time against their quality, in terms of adaptability to the environment, we find the familiar bell-shaped curve of the normal distribution. A few will be disadvantageous, leading to extinction, most will be environmentally neutral and a few will be advantageous, leading to further adaptive evolution. The driving force behind evolution is thus seen to be genetic mutation, because this is the only innate characteristic that can be passed on through inheritance. The mechanism behind mutation is still a matter of debate. Most are spontaneous, although a very few are caused by natural radiation processes. They occur only in biological systems. In the world of physics, the various elementary particles, such as electrons, are indistinguishable from each other.

Mathematically it is notable that, in two dimensions, the normal distribution takes the form of an ellipse and, in three or more dimensions, the form of a three- or multi-dimensional ellipsoid. Conic sections, it seem, appear to dominate the statistical, mechanical and electrical form of the physical universe.

As far as the parallel universe is concerned, the speculations mentioned depend upon the form in which any paranormal qualities have been demonstrated. The demonstration of telepathy or telekinesis could be the result of a new principle of physics as yet undiscovered rather than a non-physical parallel universe We have seen that Penrose has already advocated such a result as a possible explanation of consciousness. If, as seems highly unlikely, it could be conclusively demonstrated that some soul or psyche has survived bodily death, then this would almost certainly point to some kind of non-physical parallel universe. If some demonstration could be given of mental events contravening the known laws of physics, then again this would seem to point to some non-physical realm parallel to our own.

So far as I know, no convincing demonstration of any of these effects has ever been made, although all have been the subjects of clever, and not so clever, frauds practised by the devious upon the gullible. This is not surprising because, as already mentioned, if a non-physical universe indeed exists it would not be amenable to scientific investigation since its structure would be unknown to us, except perhaps through the investigation of consciousness. However, there have been honest attempts to investigate, or at least discuss this area.

Penrose himself in his book *Shadows of the Mind*, presents us with his idea of the Platonic world of mathematical forms discussed in Chapter One. He states that its existence rests on the profound, timeless and universal nature of mathematical concepts, and on the fact that the laws of mathematics are independent of those who discover them. To quote: 'The natural numbers were there before there were human beings, or indeed any other creature here on earth and they will remain after all life has perished. It has always been true that each natural number is the sum of four squares, and it did not have to wait for Lagrange to conjure this fact into existence.' Again: 'There is the mystery of how it is that perceiving beings can arise from out of the physical world. How is it that subtly organised material objects can mysteriously conjure up mental entities from out of its material substance?'

Neurological Evidence

A relevant area of research has been brought to light by Ramachandran and Blakeslee and is described in their book *Phantoms in the Brain*. It concerns a device called a transcranial magnetic stimulator. When this is applied to the scalp, it shoots a fluctuating and powerful magnetic field onto a small patch of brain tissue. This activates the patch and provides information about its function. Patients stimulated in the region of the thalamus, for example, claim to experience extreme pleasure. Patients blind from birth can see colour when the visual area of the cortex is stimulated.

It seems that when the Canadian psychologist Dr Michael Persinger used such a device to stimulate parts of the left temporal lobe of his cortex, he found that he experienced God for the first time in his life. This corresponds to the fact that patients with epileptic seizures originating in this part of the brain can have intense spiritual experiences during the seizures and sometimes become preoccupied with religion and morality, even when free of the seizure. If this somehow implies that there exists in our brain a 'God area', how did it arise? Is it a result of natural selection or is there some other mysterious explanation? Could it, for instance, indicate the existence of a non-physical intersecting universe? To quote Ramachandran:

'If religious beliefs are merely the combined result of wishful thinking and a longing for immortality how do you explain the flights of intense religious ecstasy experienced by patients with temporal lobe seizures or their claim that God speaks directly to them? Many a patient has told me of a "divine light that illuminates all things", or of an "ultimate truth that that lies completely beyond the reach of ordinary minds who are too immersed in the hustle and bustle of daily life to notice the beauty and grandeur of it all". Of course, they might be simply suffering from hallucinations and delusions of the kind that a schizophrenic might experience, but if that's the case, why do such hallucinations occur mainly when the temporal lobes are involved? Even more puzzling, why do they take this particular form? Why don't these patients hallucinate pigs or donkeys?'

Deep within the brain, there are clusters of nerve cells connected by fibre tracts. This structure, known as the limbic system, gets its input from all the sensory systems. The amygdala (Table Three) serves as the gateway to the limbic system. The output of the limbic system is mainly the experience and expression of emotions, which is mediated by back and forth connections with the frontal cortical lobes. The outward expression of these emotions requires the participation of the hypothalamus (Table One). This structure has three major outputs.

1   Hormonal and neural signals are sent to the pituitary gland (Table One). Hormones released through this system influence almost every part of the human body.

2   Commands are sent to the autonomic nervous system, which controls various bodily functions.

3   The third output drives actual behaviour, aggression, fear, feeding and sex.

Epileptic seizures in general arise because a cluster of neurons in the brain fire chaotically until the activity spreads to engulf the whole brain. In some cases, there are focal seizures that remain confined to a small patch of the brain. If such focal seizures happen to occur in the limbic system, then the symptoms are emotional and, as we have mentioned above, cause some patients to have deeply moving spiritual experiences. These include the feeling of a divine presence and a sense of communication with God. Such seizures last only for a few seconds but they can permanently alter the personality so that even between seizures the patient becomes spiritually enriched. The reason for this is not known, but Ramachandran speculates that the repeated electrical bursts inside the brain's limbic system permanently facilitate certain pathways or open new channels within the brain. This process, called kindling, might permanently alter or enrich the patient's inner emotional life. Could this be an explanation of those Old Testament prophets who 'spoke' with God or of the sudden conversion of St Paul?

Ramachandran considers that there could be four possible explanations:

1   God really does visit such people, or as I should prefer to put it, the intersection of our physical universe with the non-physical universe is referenced in some way through their consciousness.

If there is such a non-physical universe intersecting our own through consciousness, and hence the neural network, then the first explanation is quite viable, if not, then it isn't.

2   The inexplicable emotional intensity of the outburst could be misinterpreted as mystical messages from the supernatural.

This second possibility seems unlikely since there are other neurological and psychiatric disorders, like schizophrenia, in which the emotions are just as disturbed but without the intense fervour that is seen in temporal lobe epileptics. Emotional changes alone cannot completely explain the religious obsession.

3   Spurious signals stemming from limbic seizure between the sensory centres and the amygdala strengthen such salience pathways, increasing communication between brain structures by kindling. Every object and event becomes imbued with deep significance, giving the effect of spiritual or religious revelation.

The idea that 'kindling' has strengthened all the connections from the temporal cortex to the amygdala can be verified by studying the patient's galvanic skin response. If this is the case, then a patient with temporal lobe epilepsy should show an increased galvanic skin response to everything and anything. To test this idea Dr. Ramachandran, together with Dr Vincent Iragui and Dr Evelyn Tecoma, conducted the very first scientific experiment ever carried out on religious experience.

They recruited two volunteer patients showing the symptoms of this religious syndrome and attached electrodes to their hands. The volunteers were shown on a computer screen random samples of several types of words and images. They were also shown familiar faces, unfamiliar faces, erotic words and pictures, extreme violence and horror, and religious words and icons. If the kindling hypothesis were true, then the two patients would show a high response to all categories. But in fact they only showed a high response to the religious words and icons. Their response to other categories, such as sex and horror, were strangely diminished compared to that expected in normal people. Such a decrement is surprising.

It has been pointed out that not all temporal lobe epilepsy patients become religious. It depends on which parallel neural connections between the temporal cortex and the amygdala are involved. Some patients become obsessed with other subjects, such as writing, drawing and philosophy.

Whatever the final explanation, the above experiment certainly eradicates the third possibility that it is due to kindling. There is a selective enhancement of response to certain categories of stimulation such as religious words and icons and an actual reduction to other categories.

To be certain that such results imply that there are neural structures within the temporal lobes that are specialised for spirituality it would be necessary to remove a portion of a patient's temporal lobe and see if such experiences cease. Such an experiment is not viable unless the patient has some life-threatening disease in the frontal lobes, and has yet to be carried out.

One clear conclusion does emerge: there are circuits in the brain that are involved with religious experience and these become hyperactive in some epileptics.

4 The human brain has evolved specialised neural circuitry for the purpose of mediating religious experience.

Are these circuits the result of Darwinian selection effects? It would mean that at some time in the history of Homo sapiens a chance mutation of brain cells resulted in the introduction of such circuits. Following from this, the mutation would be beneficial for the survival of the species. I find this difficult to believe. That some mutations should affect and increase general intelligence through the aeons needed for evolution is obvious, given our present brain structure. That specific cultural ideas such as religion or ethics should be the result of evolutionary mutations rather than the application of already evolved intelligence seems bizarre in the extreme.

Other experiments could be envisaged. It might just be possible, using a transcranial magnetic stimulator together with a measurement of galvanic skin response, to draw certain useful conclusions regarding whether such areas of the brain exist in the higher mammals, such as chimpanzees, for example. Even better, if it were possible to conduct a similar experiment upon a person who had had no religious upbringing at all in their life, we might well gain some insight into this phenomenon.

Near-death

Another area of research involving the possibility of a non-physical parallel universe is that of the 'Near-death Experience'. Professor Michael Sabom, a cardiologist at Emory University and a staff physician at the Atlanta VA Medical Centre, has investigated this in a scientific manner. He defines a near-death event as any bodily state that causes physical unconsciousness and can reasonably be expected to result in the subject's irreversible biological death. He describes some of his findings in his book, *Recollections of Death*.

Professor Sabom and his co-workers interviewed 116 persons who had survived a near-death crisis and found that 27 per cent of them had had a 'Near-death Experience' (NDE).

There are two points worth noting in this investigation. Firstly, the evidence is necessarily anecdotal. The scientific community looks upon such evidence with suspicion because, in effect, repetition is not normally possible. Secondly, because the investigation is into 'near-death experiences', it obviously cannot be into 'death' experiences. Bearing these two points in mind, let us look at some of his findings.

> *Ineffability*. People had great difficulty in describing their near-death experiences and were, in general, unable to find relevant analogies.

> *Timelessness*. All intuitive sense of the time duration of the experience was lost.

> *Reality*. A strong sense of reality pervaded the experience.

> *Sense of death*. A sense of being dead or dying came early in the experience.

> *Emotional tranquillity*. There was a feeling of calm and tranquillity during the experience in contrast to the physical pain suffered when in a conscious state immediately prior to or following the experience.

> *Body Separation*. It was felt that the experience had taken place outside the physical body (autoscopic experience).

Preceding the feeling of tranquillity, the basic experience seemed to consist of a feeling of being enclosed in darkness. More than half of the patients described a brilliant source of light signalling the end of the dark region. Many of the patients also described scenes of scenic beauty and encounters with others, including, sometimes, God Himself.

The experience ended with a feeling of having returned to one's body, often under the influence of another spiritual being.

No significant difference in the NDE was found with respect to differing social or educational standards of the 116 patients. It also seemed to be unaffected by the different near-death situations encountered.

The study found that persons who had had a NDE had a lower death anxiety (measured by the Templer and Dickstein death anxiety scales) than those who had had no such experience.

Explanations of the NDE take various forms.

1 That human, or for that matter any conscious brain, really is dualistic and the mind-brain split explains the autoscopic and/or transcendental experience.

2 The above experiences, although not dualistic, are in some way connected with a non-physical parallel universe intersecting our physical universe through universal consciousness.

3 The piecing together of aurally perceived information by a semi-conscious patient activates an accurate picture of ongoing events such as resuscitation efforts.

4 The NDE is in fact a conscious fabrication by persons taking advantage of the investigator.

5 It is a subconscious fabrication caused by the human need to survive.

6 It is an autoscopic hallucination similar in effect to those of schizophrenia, whereby the patient will suddenly see an image of himself or herself projected in front of them.

7 It is the result of dreams caused by the NDE itself.

8 It could be drug-induced hallucinations, although not all persons reporting NDEs were on drugs at the time.

9 It could be temporal lobe seizure caused by epileptogenic discharges in the temporal lobes.

10 Hypoxia caused by lowered oxygen blood level has been known to cause hallucinations.

11 Hypercarbia caused by elevated levels of carbon dioxide in the brain can cause a wide variety of hallucinogenic experience.

Professor Sabom deals with all these explanations in great detail. The last one is the closest to a purely physical explanation. However, one measurement was made of the blood oxygen and carbon dioxide levels at the time of a patient's cardiac arrest and NDE. The oxygen level was elevated and the carbon dioxide level depressed, which seems to contradict the hypoxia and hypercarbia theories.

The Christian Research Institute report that the medical and scientific communities largely discount the claims that NDEs indicate there is life after death. Although their explanations are diverse, most of them are sceptical of out-of-body experiences and the associated visions. Nevertheless, few would dispute that a dramatic psychological effect has occurred with those who have reported an NDE.

Dr Robert Jordan has developed a theory which parallels the physiology of the dying process. He states on the Internet:

'The theory presented here is not intended as a materialist or reductionist interpretation of spiritual experiences. I do not believe that it invalidates anyone's religious belief or spiritual experience. It is merely a parallel physical explanation of some of the commonly reported experiential phenomena of NDEs. A basic outline of the proposed theory of NDEs follows:

William James and Carl Lange's *Theory of Emotions* undergirds the present theory of near-death experiences. Their theory states that the experience of emotion depends fundamentally upon the brain's processing of feedback from the body's peripheral sensory stimulation. For example, one's experience of anxiety is due primarily to the brain's processing of feedback from pervasive skeletal muscle tension as well as feedback from the arousal of internal organs, primarily the heart and circulatory system.

When people (as well as animals) die, we do so from the periphery towards the center of the body. The heart stops pumping blood and we stop breathing. Our sensory (proprioceptive) awareness of feeling in the extremities of the body, that is, legs and arms, would cease first. Effectively, the extremities would become numb to sensation.'

Next, we would lose awareness of the proprioceptive feedback from the skin, bones, and muscles of the trunk, neck and head. Simultaneously, we would lose awareness of the proprioceptive feedback from the internal organs, including the reproductive organs, heart, lungs, and digestive tract. The experiential correlate of this cut-off of peripheral feedback from skin, muscles, bone, and internal organs would be the frequently reported near-death-experience sense of detached floating, an awareness no longer bound by the sense of an attached body.

The core senses associated with the head, such as vision, hearing and smell, are neurally very closely connected to the brain. With these senses still functioning, we would be able to hear environmental sounds and conversations of nearby people and see the events surrounding our own deaths. Again, we would feel detached from these events because we would have little or no sense of emotion in the absence of peripheral and proprioceptive sensory feedback.

Finally, we would lose awareness of the sensory feedback from the primary senses associated with the head, including vision, hearing, taste, and smell. This loss of sensory feedback might correlate with near-death-experience reports of passing through a long dark tunnel.

When all organs of sensation have ceased functioning, the brain would still continue to function for some seconds or minutes afterwards. (Of course, the brain itself has no sensory capacity, including no capacity to communicate pain or discomfort to itself.) As with the rest of the body, the brain's dying follows the general principal of cessation of functioning moving from the periphery towards the centre.

The last vestiges of awareness to remain would be due to stimulation of the earliest and most entrenched primal memories, devoid of any emotionality in the form of sensory feedback. These memories would be stimulated to recall by spontaneous firing of neurons.

The pineal gland at the very centre of the brain would be one of the last organs of the brain to cease functioning.

Before the pineal gland actually ceased to function, spontaneous firing of its neurons would produce a sensation of light. One's awareness of the light would be particularly sensitised because there would be no external sensory input to compete with it. The more peripheral brain functions of speech, logical thought, and interpretation would have ceased to function earlier in the progression of the brain's death process.

I read Dr Karl Jansen's description of the effects of ketamines in producing near-death experiences. Moderate doses of ketamines can temporarily cause the body's peripheral sensory feedback to the brain to diminish or shut down, hence its effectiveness as a general anaesthetic. His description of the physical changes that ketamine causes in the body and the brain seems to support the present model for near-death experiences.'

This seems to be a reasonably convincing explanation of an experience of death rather than near-death. How recovery could occur when the major part of the brain is dead, I cannot imagine. It could only happen if the brain was alive but incapacitated in some way. Does the pineal gland actually fire neurons to produce a sensation of light? I was under the impression that the pineal gland was sensitive to light, which reduces the amount of melatonin secreted, thus causing wakefulness, as opposed to sleep, when the melatonin is high.

The whole subject of the 'Near-Death Experience' is strange and of course attracts the 'New Age' pundits, or what I would call The Abracadabra Brigade. There is a vast store of information on the Internet for those interested.

I personally do not believe that the NDE proves the existence of an 'afterlife' but it could have some bearing on an intersecting non-physical universe, if such is the case.

Other scientific experiments into the paranormal e.g. telepathy do not seem to have produced any startling results. As far as I know, the measure of any reported significance is too small to be convincing.

Summary

This chapter investigates the most mysterious concept of all, consciousness. The difficulties in understanding such a concept and various associated ideas are discussed. The cosmological idea of a parallel universe intersecting our own through consciousness is postulated. The theory considers that such a parallel universe could be different from our own, not only in construction but also in kind. If the intersection of the universes is consciousness, then conflict within the parallel universe could be reflected in our own, thus forming the basis of religious dualism.

The parallel universe is equated with the idea of the supernatural. The difficulty of finding scientific evidence in this field, with its plethora of frauds and cheats, is appreciated.

Various theories of consciousness, for example, those of Dennett, and, in particular, Penrose are described.

An elementary description of the brain and some of its main functions are given in order to assist the reader in following the ideas of Penrose, and the neurological observations of Dr V S Ramachandran. Certain of these observations could indicate, in some respects, the concept of a parallel universe intersecting consciousness through the brain's temporal lobes.

The final section of the chapter describes some research conducted by Professor Michael Sabom into examples of near-death experience. It is supplemented by possible explanations of the phenomenon, including a detailed exposition by Dr Robert Jordan.

Chapter Nine

Conclusions

What is reality?

It is an established fact that all the main world religions, both Eastern and Western, were formulated in the pre-Copernican age. The Copernican revolution has seriously undermined the Western Religions, but has not really affected the Eastern religions to anything like the same extent.

Hinduism

Hinduism regards humanity as part of a cosmic whole (with or without God or gods), which involves respect for life in all its manifestations. Individualism is rejected. There is a demand for meditation and a strict discipline such as yoga so that the individual may re-integrate into the whole universe. In such a religion, it does not really matter whether there is only one world containing life or billions of them. Since it is not anthropocentric, man is not the measure of all things. In fact, the vastness of the universe would enhance rather than detract from such a religion.

Sikhs

The Sikh faith is intensely communal and the religious teaching is intensely personal. Sikhs believe in one God who is called the True

Creator, free from fear and hate, immortal, not begotten, self-existent, great and compassionate. The True was at the beginning, the True was in the distant past, the True is at the present and the True will also be in the future.

They consider that people are blinded to the true nature of life by materialism, and the only hope for sinful people is in the mercy of God. He will grant to the true seeker a sense of the divine presence, which lifts him or her from a life of material bondage. Salvation is a love union with God and individuals must be reincarnated many times before such a union can take place. Their holy book, *The Guru Granth*, is not an explanation of beliefs but stimulates the love of God. The Sikh religion is both an ethical and an ethnic religion, seeking to maintain and honour the community. It does not deny the truths of other faiths.

Such a religion is unlikely to be affected by the discoveries of cosmology and can take the progress of modern cosmology in its stride. After all, the belief in reincarnation and the existence of a Designer Creator can easily extend through an infinite universe, although reincarnation is not a belief in line with modern scientific thought.

Jainism

We have already mentioned Jainism, the religion that believes in a universe that passes through an infinite number of cosmic cycles and contains an infinite number of transmigrating souls. Certain aspects of modern cosmology, for instance the idea of eternal inflation, would fit very well into this religion, especially as there is no belief in a Divine Creator as such. It should be noted that this highly ethical religion does not need almighty God as the source of ethics. After all, if the universe does not need a Creator why should ethical values need one?

Parsis

The Parsis are in effect the remains of the Zoroastrians. Today, there are only about 200,000 of them, mostly in Bombay. Their ancient beliefs are anthropocentric, since the six creations of God – cattle, fire, earth, metal, water and plants – culminated in the seventh creation, humankind, as the representative of God. As in the Western Religions, the Copernican Principle would invalidate this. In modern times, however, many of the Parsis have studied in Europe and America. This has affected their reform movements, which in some cases have even denied that revelation is a valid religious concept, because a truth learned for oneself is understood better than one imposed from above. Thus, this small but influential community does seem to have been affected by modern teachings. Intriguingly enough, the orthodox backlash against these modernists involves theosophy, which originated with the Theosophical Society, founded by Madam Blavatsky in 1875. It comprised a mix of Hindu, Buddhist and Christian ideas with stress on reincarnation, immortality and the presence of God in all things. Theosophists also believed in a series of world teachers who are incarnated to express the divine wisdom. Behramshah Shroff instigated a particular form of Parsi theosophy early in the twentieth century, preaching the Ilm-I Kshnoom, the path of knowledge, but the majority of Parsis practise their ancient religion in the knowledge of its basic ideals.

Buddhism

Siddarther Gautama, who lived in India in the sixth century BC, founded Buddhism. He had a mystical experience after seven years of dedicated meditation in the forests. It was while he was sitting under the Bodhi (enlightenment) tree that he suddenly obtained the final enlightenment that made him the Buddha (the awakened).

Immediately after his awakening, he went to the Deer Park of

Benares to preach to his fellow hermits. He first preached the Four Noble Truths:

1 Suffering and frustration come from resisting the flow of life.

2 The self is an illusion since the ultimate reality is one.

3 The cause of all suffering is the clinging to and grasping of life.

4 Following the eightfold path to Buddhahood can end suffering and frustration.

According to Buddha, every part of the universe is subject to change and decay, everything that is created must perish. This belief is easily compatible with the Second Law of Thermodynamics. The basic goal of the Buddhist is to be freed from the endless cycle of rebirth and attain Nirvana. This is accomplished by following the noble eightfold Path which formed Buddha's basic teaching and constitute the ethical component of Buddhism. These eight signposts to freedom are as follows:

1 Right knowledge of the existence, the origin, the destruction and the removal of suffering.

2 Right attitude of goodwill and peacefulness and a rejection of hate and malice.

3 Right speech of truth and reconciliation.

4 Right action of the moral imperative.

5 Right occupation, excluding harm to others.

6 Right effort towards noble thoughts, words and deeds.

7   Right mindfulness, abjuring the dictates of evil
     desires.

8   Right composure, which is achieved by intense
     concentration, facilitating the holy man's quest for
     Nirvana.

It is informative to read the description of Nirvana given in the
Tripitaka, an early Buddhist scripture.

'Nirvana is the area where there is no earth, water, fire
and air. It is not the region of infinite space, nor that of
infinite consciousness. It is not the region of nothing at
all, nor is it the border between distinguishing and not
distinguishing. Neither this world nor the other world.
Where there is neither sun nor moon. I will not call it
coming and going, nor standing still, nor fading away
nor beginning. It is without foundation, without
continuation and without stopping. It is the end of
suffering.'

This could easily be a poetic description of the non-physical
parallel universe postulated in the last chapter. Since none of the
laws or constituents of our physical universe apply, it can only be
described by negatives.

It can be seen that this religion would easily correlate with some
of the concepts of modern cosmology.

After the death of Buddha, the religion developed into two main
schools: the Hinyana, prevalent in Sri Lanka, Thailand and Burma,
which follows the teaching of Buddha in a strictly orthodox sense;
and the Mahayana, which became established in Tibet, Nepal, China
and Japan. It is a more flexible version following the spirit of his
teachings rather than the letter.

The Hinyana was first written down after five hundred years
of oral transmission. Known as the Pali Cannon, it was written in

the Pali language in the first century AD. The Mahayana was written in Sanskrit about two hundred years later in the form of sutras (scriptures).

Buddhism is, as we have seen, an atheistic religion, dedicated to the release from reincarnation and the attainment of Nirvana by following the eightfold path. Modern cosmological theories are easily incorporated into such a belief. The existence of alien life throughout the universe presents no problems.

Confucianism

The Chinese religions of Confucianism and Taoism are indeed anthropocentric but in an ethical or mystical rather than a cosmological sense.

Confucianism derives from a highly regarded teacher, Kung Fu Tzu, who transmitted the ancient heritage to his disciples. His teachings were based upon the *Six Classics,* ancient scripts of philosophy, poetry, history and music, representing China's past traditions. His ideas were promulgated through a collection of aphorisms compiled by his disciples. They are known as the *Confucian Analects.*

The name Confucianism was first coined by the seventeenth-century Jesuit missionaries who recognised the religious nature of Confucianism, although it was regarded mainly as a moral philosophy. Confucian moral metaphysics reaches into the religious quest for unity with the ground of existence. Although most of Confucius' teachings put great stress upon human ethics, he made it clear that heaven or God gave him his message. He stands as a prophet, giving moral teachings firmly grounded in religious consciousness. In its mystical vision of the unity of the universe, Confucianism is in fact pantheistic. Such a religion would have no difficulty incorporating the concepts of a vast, diverse and possibly infinite universe.

Taoism

Taoism is a much more mystical religion than Confucianism. It undertakes the contemplation of nature, seeking unity with the Tao, a metaphysical absolute deriving from an earlier personal God. This unity is achieved by passive acceptance and mystical contemplation.

These were the teachings of Lao-tzu and Chuang-tzu, the great Taoist teachers. They were interested in intuition rather than logic. They had great contempt for reasoning and argumentation. The Taoists considered them part of an artificial subjective world. They were concerned fully with the observation of nature, which led them to the belief that transformation, growth and decay, implicitly reside in all things. They believed in acting spontaneously, in harmony with nature. They saw all natural changes as the manifestation of opposites, which are in essence aspects of the same things. This particularly applies to economic activity and the relativity of moral standards. It is easy to see how Marxist dialectic materialism could appeal to such a mindset.

Their texts served a later generation of adherents whose purpose was to obtain the secret of life itself and so achieve immortality. They practised a ritual of prayer and appeasement combined with yoga and meditation. This new religion was called Taoist to distinguish it from the philosophy of Lao-tzu and Chuang-tzu.

All the various schools and sects of Taoism were in one sense or another seeking freedom: freedom from political constraints or freedom from death or freedom in unity with the Tao. The Tao is the principle of the universe as well as a pattern for human behaviour. The Tao is not a conscious god. The Creator cannot have a conscious mind. Creation takes place spontaneously. The breath and matter unite, coagulate and become shape. Constant with transformation it continues without ever ceasing.

This could easily be a poetic description of modern 'Big Bang' cosmology.

Religions of Japan

Religion in Japan mainly consists of the imported religions of Confucianism and Buddhism in addition to the native Shinto faith. This includes a wide conglomeration of practices rooted in prehistoric Japan, originally animist in their simplest form.

The imperial household, whose ancestry supposedly originated in the sun goddess, took a central position within Shinto. At the end of the Second World War, the emperor's divine status was officially revoked and Shinto disestablished.

Modern Shinto is based on individual shrines, each of which has some individual reason for its existence, either natural or historical. Shinto practice is a matter for each individual. It includes a rinse of purification and a worship hall where petitionary prayers are made. The most important feature of Shinto is the festival, during which, a particular shrine takes on a meaning for all its worshipers at the same time. This usually includes a procession, or a fair with stalls and side shows.

Shinto appears to be a purely local religion based on local superstition. The findings of science, with respect to cosmology or anything else, would not affect it in any way.

Mysticism and Science

The main reason why Eastern Religions can take modern cosmology in their stride is that their associated philosophies aim for the direct mystical experience of reality. Although differing in details, the overall view of these religions is of the unity and relatedness of all constructs in the universe. All things are seen in terms of a cosmic oneness. They consider that our categorisation of separate objects and events is an illusion maintained to help us cope with our environment. The main aim of the eastern mystical process is to readjust our minds, by means of meditation, to the ultimate unity of the universe.

Fritjof Capra, in his book *The Tao of Physics*, points out that this bears a remarkable similarity to modern particle physics. Quantum physics cannot separate the observed from the observer; all observed events have to include the effect of the observer. Capra states that 'participator' should replace the word 'observer' since in some sense we inhabit a participatory universe, an idea culminating in the physicist's search for 'the theory of everything'. Such an idea is well known to students of eastern mysticism; not in the form of quantum mechanics, but in the sense that only with the participation of one's whole being can mystical knowledge be obtained.

Like physics, eastern religions regard the overall unity of the universe in a dynamic sense. Everything is flowing and changing. This philosophical idea blends well with the evolving and expanding universe of modern cosmology.

The main difference between the ideas of the eastern mystics and those of modern physics is that, in many cases, the latter are well defined mathematically. This allows us to take advantage of them and construct modern technology, benefiting whole populations that would otherwise live in abject poverty. Eastern mysticism, although corresponding to modern physics in many ways, abjures definition. The ability to obtain insight and mystical experience through meditation is limited to a small minority of the eastern population. Most people in the Far East, especially India and Pakistan, are too busy trying to survive to practise mystical meditation. It is ironic that rising living standards in the east will be brought about by western technology that may allow more of their populations the freedom to practise their own definition-defying religion of meditation and mysticism.

The Western Religions

When we come to the three Western Religions, in chronological order, Judaism, Christianity and Islam, we find them in their fundamentalist capacity, starkly antithetical to modern cosmology.

Judaism

In Judaism, from which the other two religions sprang, mankind is the central issue. Among mankind, the Jews, created to enlighten the world, take centre stage in the divine plan. God personally dictated to Moses their holy book, the Torah (consisting of the first five books of the Old Testament). The first book, Genesis, tells of the creation of the world, the creation of life and the first man and woman, Adam and Eve. It relates the conflict between Cain and Able, the genealogies from Adam to Noah, the flood, the story of Abraham (the first Jew), the binding of Abraham's son Isaac, the story of Jacob who became Israel and the story of Joseph.

The second book, Exodus, deals with the enslavement of the Israelites in Egypt, their eventual liberation through God's will, and, following Moses, their exodus towards Israel, the Promised Land. The giving of the Ten Commandments at Sinai during the exodus forms the basis of western ethical law.

The Torah continues with Leviticus, a book of orthodox Jewish law, including directions for sacrifice and rules of ritual defilement and purification. Nearly all these laws ceased to function when the Temple was destroyed in AD70. They have no relevance to the conduct of even the most strictly orthodox Jew today. When the Messiah arrives, however, the Temple will be rebuilt and these laws will again come into effect. Prayers for this restoration are in the orthodox prayer book.

The fourth book, Numbers, is composed of narrative, legislation and archival records. It starts at just a little over a year after the children of Israel came out of Egypt and covers the years of their wandering in the desert. It is sometimes called by the Hebrew name *Bemidbar* meaning 'in the wilderness'. The law usually given is case law, arising from certain circumstances in the narrative. For example, the story of the dedication of the Tabernacle gives rise to the statement of priestly obligations and privileges. From these local laws the Torah proceeds to state the more general laws valid for eternity.

The fifth and final book, Deuteronomy, is presented as a series of farewell speeches by Moses, and ends with a description of his death. It contains a flow of narrative, exhortation, liturgy, law and poetry. It addresses Israel at an historic moment, aiming at national solutions to achieve peace and prosperity.

The remainder of the Bible consists of the Prophets and the Writings, which do not concern us here.

The other main religious books of the Jews are the *Talmud*, adding extra laws to the biblical laws, the *Mishna*, another collection of laws compiled by Judah the Prince in about 200BC, and the *Gemara*, a collection of rabbinical discussions based on the *Mishna*.

From the point of view of orthodox belief, the Torah is the word of God given in some unspecified way to Moses. Every sentence and every paragraph reproduces the divine truth. Because it is the word of God, the Torah is 'holy writ' and not one letter can be changed or omitted. But its contents are totally at odds with modern scientific knowledge. To the orthodox, as we discussed in Chapter Two, this means that either our science is erroneous or we lack understanding of the Torah.

From the point of view of progressive Judaism, these ancient books contain a wealth of wisdom and advice and indeed form a basis for discussion, argument and interpretation. The ethics contained therein are similar in most ways to those of the Eastern religions discussed above. Of course, the books of the Torah are not meant to be scientific or even historic, although they include many historic events. They are books of religion, morals, ethics and legislation. Nevertheless, a fundamental precept of the religion is the central place of the Jews in bringing the knowledge of the one true God to mankind, as well as the central place of mankind within the universe. In Liberal Judaism the concept of the Jews as God's chosen people is not emphasised since it is recognised that other religions also make some claim to divine exclusivity. Nevertheless, even an atheist must admit that the Jews first introduced transcendent monotheism as a religious, rather than a philosophical concept.

Our first three chapters argue the fallacy of orthodox belief in the light of modern cosmology and the Copernican Principle. Man, in effect, has been demoted to one intelligent species among billions or possibly even an infinite number. In this respect, Judaism, together with its two religious offspring, Christianity and (to a certain extent) Islam is on a par with C S Lewis's local religion of 'savages'. This demonstrates that even certain elements of progressive Judaism, although chronologically post-Copernican, are still pre-Copernican in their fundamental attitudes.

It is true that nowhere in Genesis does it state that earth is the only planet in God's creation, yet it is implicit in the creation story and in the succeeding chapters. This is for the very good reason that at the time of writing the concept of the modern cosmos was unknown. In pre-Copernican times, the idea of the house of Israel being a light unto nations, leading the world to the knowledge of the one true God, was a valid and noble ideal. In the light of present scientific knowledge, being one chosen race among billions of other possible chosen races on other life-bearing planets does not have anything like the same grandeur.

Christianity

Christianity, like Orthodox Judaism, still exists in a mental pre-Copernican universe. It is shown by belief in the incarnation, the divine sacrifice, the second coming and the resurrection of the dead, on our insignificant little planet in a universe teeming with intelligent life, even if there is only one example per galaxy.

The exclusivity of Judaism has passed over to Christianity in the form of Christian belief that redemption is possible through Christ alone. "I am the way, the truth, and the life: no man cometh unto the Father but by me." (St John 14: 6) Unlike Islam, there is no allowance for other religions or beliefs, even though Jesus said, "For he that is not against us is on our part." (St Mark 9: 40)

In mainstream Christianity, even among its most enlightened followers, the fundamental beliefs of the incarnation and the resurrection are de rigueur. 'And if Christ be not risen, then is our preaching vain, and your faith is also vain.' (St Paul, Corinthians 15: 14) In pre-Copernican times, the incarnation of God in the person of Jesus seemed to be the climax of all history, although it must be noted that Jesus himself never claimed to be God incarnate. That the chosen house of Israel should be extended through belief in Jesus to the whole of humanity was the fulfilment of the divine Messianic prophecy, to be succeeded almost immediately by the second coming of Christ . ('Verily I say unto you, this generation shall not pass away, till all be fulfilled.' Luke 21: 32; Mark 14: 30; Matthew 25: 34) Unfortunately He did not come. The faithful still wait and look likely to continue to wait for a considerable time. Modern cosmology has shown that creation, if creation there was, is far too extensive to be subject to a local god on some insignificant planet.

Islam

Islam originated as an Arab religion. Originally, the Arabs were pagans who worshipped a pantheon of gods ruled by al-Lah, whose name simply means the 'High God'. These Arabs were divided into various tribes in constant warfare with each other. They lived by an ideology known as *Muruwah*, which in effect means courage, endurance and dedication to the tribe. The vendetta was endemic and comprised a rough form of justice preventing the dominance of any one tribe.

In the fifth century, some of the Syrian Arabs rediscovered the presumed authentic monotheistic religion of Abraham, who had lived before the coming of the Torah or the Gospels. He was therefore considered by them to be neither Jew nor Christian.

The method of worshipping this one true God only became known, however, in the year AD610, with the revelations of Muhammad ibn Abdullah on the seventeenth night of Ramadan, then a pagan festival.

According to Muhammad, he was visited by an angel of the Lord and ordered to 'recite'. Three times the order was given and only after two refusals did Muhammad give way and recite the first words of what was to form the Koran, which in English means the *Recitation*.

Concerned that he may have been possessed by a demon, Muhammad contemplated suicide but was eventually reassured by the Angel Gabriel that he was indeed God's messenger. This was confirmed by consultation with his cousin Waraqa ibn Nawfal, a Christian who was an expert in the Holy Scriptures. He assured Muhammad that he was indeed the prophet of Allah. After some years, Muhammad, now convinced, started his divine task by preaching to his tribe, the *Quraysh* in the Arabic language. The Koran itself was revealed to Muhammad over a period of twenty-three years, each revelation constituting a struggle of understanding and interpretation.

Muhammad himself, although of exceptional gifts, was not an educated man. He could neither read nor write so he recited the Koran aloud. Some of his followers (the reciters) committed it to memory, while the more literate of them, especially chosen by the prophet, wrote it down. The first compilation was made some twenty years after the death of Muhammad. This was the task undertaken during the Caliphate of Abu Bakr (AD632-634). It was entrusted to the scribe Zayed Ibn Thabit after the battle of Yamamah, where many of the reciters were killed. Zayed, with the help of companions, accomplished the task of collating and writing the first authenticated version of the Koran. This copy was kept at the residence of Hafsah, wife of the Prophet. The successor to Abu Bakr was Uthman (AD644-656). He ordered Zayed and his assistants to make perfect copies of this authenticated version. Copies were sent to various destinations in the Muslim empire, while the original copy was returned to Hasfah. A copy was also kept at Medina. Although this time lapse would almost certainly have led to some corruption of the original recitation, my Muslim correspondents assure me that because of the meticulous method of compilation, any such corruption would be of a very low level.

In fact, the *Quraysh* already believed in God or al-Lah, the maker of heaven and earth, actually the same God worshipped by Jews and the Christian. What Muhammad taught them, and eventually all the Arab tribes, was their duty towards God and their recognition of His benevolence. The Koran teaches that it is good to share the wealth of the community in a fair manner and not to hoard riches for one's own benefit. Society must be just and equitable. God is transcendent and experienced as a moral imperative.

Muslims were taught by the Koran to use reason in their study of the natural world to determine the signs of God. Hence, a tradition of natural science was not deemed antagonistic to religion, as was the case with Christianity. In spite of present appearances, the Muslim religion is much more tolerant than either Judaism or Christianity. There are no obligatory doctrines about God and theological speculation is dismissed as self-indulgent guesswork. God is experienced as the moral imperative. In the Koran, God is more impersonal than the God of the Jews. Something of Him can be faintly discerned in the natural world but he is so transcendent that he cannot be discussed except in parables. The Koran is not considered to eliminate the messages of previous prophets but embodies the continuing religious experience of mankind. Muhammad only aimed at the conversion of the polytheistic Arabs. He never asked Jews or Christians to convert unless they wished to do so, since they had also received authentic revelations from God.

> 'And argue not with the people of the scripture, Jews and Christians, unless it be in a way that is better with good words and in good manner, inviting them to Islamic Monotheism with his verses, except with such of them as do wrong; and say to them: "We believe in that which has been revealed to us and revealed to you: our God and your God is One and to Him we have submitted as Muslims." '

> Koran (Surah: 29 Surat Al-'Ankabut: 46)

This compares favourably with orthodox Jewish exclusivity or the Christian imperative 'to believe in Christ to be saved'.

The Koran also instructs that there is to be no forcible conversion to Islam, and that war is evil and abhorrent, and must only be undertaken in self-defence.

And it also insists upon the complete equality of the sexes. The old pagan practice of female infanticide was strictly forbidden and dismay at the birth of a daughter rather than a son was severely reprimanded. The emancipation of women was an important part of Muhammad's revelation. For example, the Koran gives women legal rights of inheritance and divorce. The veil is not prescribed for all women but only for the wives of Muhammad, as a status symbol.

The present inferior status of women in many Muslim states is due not to the Islamic faith but to reactionary pre-Koranic tradition and negative misinterpretation of the holy texts.

The reading of the Koran to Muslims in the original Arabic is a spiritual experience. The chanting of its verses in the mosque gives them the same transcendental feeling that listening to an oratorio or Gregorian chant gives to Christians. The same can be said of the Hebrew liturgy and psalms recited in the synagogue.

What, then, can be said of the effect of modern cosmology upon the Muslim faith?

The fundamentalist beliefs of Islam, the messianic tradition, the concept of Judgement Day, the Prophet's paradise with its houris, etc. are invalidated by the Copernican Principle in the same way that the beliefs of Judaism and Christianity are. Nevertheless, apart from its fundamentalist aspect, Islam does not have the same literal interpretation of events that we find in Christianity or Judaism. There are sophisticated arguments that nevertheless involve special pleading, that the accounts of Judgement Day, the joys of paradise and the terrors of hell are not meant to be interpreted literally but as expressions of some higher reality transcending the world. The objections to these beliefs that we described in Chapter Three refer to our own physical universe and therefore do not really apply. This is a fascinating argument but still leaves us with a belief in the intervention of God in human history, the giving of the Koran itself for instance. This does not necessarily negate the Copernican Principle but it is certainly at odds with the ideas of modern science, which abjures such intervention.

Although the Copernican Principle invalidates Islamic fundamentalism, the mystical element of such a religion can be examined apart from any orthodox insistence on fundamentals. In effect, this eliminates the idea of a personal God and brings in the conception of God as transcendent. We are almost back to the God of Aristotle. The beliefs of Muslim mystics such as the Sufis have a great deal in common with the Throne Mysticism of the Jewish Kabbalah.

God is transcendent and forms part of a paramount reality that cannot be described in words but can only be experienced by the mystic, with the aid of the techniques and disciplines – fasting, night vigils, chanting holy names as a mantra – perfected by the Sufis.

Such mysticism cannot be affected by science, although neurological explanations may be possible in time. Certainly modern cosmology would have no impact upon the mystical tradition that is particularly evident in the Muslim religion. Like the other two Western monotheistic religions, Islam is pre-Copernican. However, if modern cosmology were taken into account, the tradition of transcendental interpretation of the Koran and the emphasis on the use of reason and evidence in the investigation of nature would greatly mitigate the effect of the Copernican revolution upon its devotees. In fact, there is no evidence of any Muslim religious opposition to the Copernican Principle. For this reason, the secularisation of Judaism and the marginalisation of mainstream Christianity have no real counterpart in Islam.

Religion and the Parallel Universe

From a cosmological standpoint, the concept of a parallel universe intersecting our own physical universe through consciousness is a valid speculation. In many ways, it conforms to religious ideas throughout the world, in both the present and the past. Unfortunately, it conforms too well. The idea can be used to explain almost anything that is considered to be supernatural: From heaven and hell to telepathy and psychokinesis, from Nirvana to ghosts and phantoms, and in general all mystical and religious experiences, genuine or otherwise. The only scientific grasp we could have on such a universe would be through neurology. Future experiments in this field might give us some indication of the manner in which our cosmos is constructed. For example, if the left temporal lobes of other conscious species were stimulated, what would be the effect? What could we deduce from the behaviour of chimpanzees or dolphins under the effect of such stimulation? I await with interest any such experiments.

Ethics as an Emergent Property

I do not postulate the above concept of a parallel universe as a Deistic argument, although it could be used as such. I am merely using the ideas and speculations of the multi-universe cosmology in the attempt to explain in some way the existence and evolution of sentience and consciousness throughout the cosmos. If we consider the parallel universe to be the source of emergent properties like consciousness and self-organisation, could it not also be the source of ethics and aesthetics as a self-emergent process?

Three hundred years ago, Thomas Hobbes argued that, before government existed, the state of nature was governed by selfish individuals who competed with such vicious ruthlessness that life was nasty, brutish, solitary and short. He considered that some kind of strong central authority is necessary to enforce co-operation. Since then there have been various arguments as to whether this was necessarily correct. Could co-operation possibly emerge without the impact of a central authority?

There are many situations where there is a conflict between self-interest and the common good. The challenge is to find a mathematical method of representing this situation in general rather than investigating the thousands of separate cases that occur.

In 1950, Merrill Flood and Melvin Dresher discovered such a method using a very old puzzle known as The Prisoner's Dilemma. It is a branch of game theory and was formalised by A W Tucker of Princeton University.

The easiest way to describe this game is to consider two prisoners, each faced with the choice of giving evidence against the other and so reducing his own sentence. If neither defects upon the other, they can both be convicted but on a lesser charge and given three years. If they both defect and give evidence against each other, then they will both be convicted on the more serious charge and given five years. If only one defects and gives evidence against the other, then the defector will have his sentence reduced to two years while the prisoner who remained silent would be convicted on the more serious charge and given six years. It seems that both would be better off if they co-operated with each other by remaining silent, but each could be individually better off if he defects. Consider two prisoners A and B. If A chooses to co-operate with B by remaining silent, but B defects, then A gets six years and B gets two years. If A defects and B defects, then they both get five years. B then is better off defecting, whatever A does. Since A could use the same argument, the certain outcome is mutual defection, both getting five years each, when they could have mutually co-operated and received three years each. The logically best action in a moral vacuum is to defect. Selfishness is the rational answer.

Any situation in which you are tempted to act in a certain way but realise it would be a mistake if everybody else so acted is a Prisoner's Dilemma. This is the mathematical idealisation of the conflict between collective and individual interests. The conclusion that defection is the logical answer to The Prisoner's Dilemma appears to be at odds with the way people behave in the real world where co-operation seems to be the norm.

In 1979, a political scientist, Robert Axelrod asked people to submit a computer program to play The Prisoner's Dilemma 200 times against every other program submitted. At the end of the contest, each program would have scored a number of points. If both players co-operate with each other, they are awarded three points each (the reward for mutual co-operation). If one player co-operates and the other defects, then the defecting player gets five points (the temptation to defect) and the co-operating player gets no points (the sucker's payoff). If both defect, each get one point (the punishment for mutual defection).

Fourteen people submitted programs of differing complexity. The program that came out top was one called *TIT FOR TAT*, written by Anatol Rapoport, a Canadian political scientist. It was the simplest of them all. It began by co-operating and then copying its opponent's last tactic. Further, more extensive tournaments were held and again *TIT FOR TAT* was victorious. The success of this program was due to mutual co-operation, its avoidance of unnecessary conflict, retaliation in the face of defection, forgiveness after retaliation and clarity of behaviour. It seems that mutual defection is the norm when the game is played only once. In real life, where the situation is normally encountered many times, co-operation becomes the norm. It could now be seen that, under suitable conditions, co-operation in society in the form of reciprocity could develop naturally without a central authority to enforce it.

It is interesting that co-operation can arise in different environments and that the individuals involved do not have to be rational. The evolutionary process allows successful co-operating strategies to thrive even when the players do not know why or how. Altruism is not needed. Beginning in small clusters, the level of co-operation tends to go up and not down. This illustrates the Darwinian evolution of co-operation in the animal kingdom culminating in the human discipline of ethics.

That this could indeed be the case is shown by instances of co-operation among other species. Frans de Waal writes of the *TIT FOR TAT* phenomenon among chimpanzees; and Manfred Milinsky has even observed it among stickleback fish.

Co-operation thus emerges from the evolution of reciprocity and becomes something greater. It leads to altruism and the magnificent ethical works of literature that we find in religions – the Bible, the Koran, the *Vedas*, the *Pali Canon,* etc. As such, it becomes an emergent property. It follows that ethics could emerge through a parallel universe from subjective instinct to objective values.

An analogy can be made with the concept of colour. Colour, as we commonly recognise it, does not exist in our physical universe. There are different frequencies of electromagnetic radiation, and colour is produced in the visual system of the brain to distinguish those that are important for survival. For example, natural selection would favour individuals that can distinguish between predator and prey by means of colour differentiation. In the human species, at least, the practical value of colour has evolved into something more. It enables us to appreciate the aesthetic value of great works of art such as the Sistine Chapel. Colour has emerged in our minds from a survival aid to an aesthetic experience, which in itself appears to have no survival value whatever.

There are, of course, unfortunate individuals who are colour-blind and, tragically for society, there are individuals who suffer from moral blindness. When such individuals possess great power, they become responsible for unnecessary wars and massacres. In general, such significant ethical principles as the support of kin, obligations of reciprocity, constraints on sexual relations, and limitations on violence are held in every human community, manifesting themselves even in the most difficult circumstances. They also affect the lives of many of the higher animals.

Ethical Reductionism Questioned

The logical positivists, such as A J Ayer, hold to a purely reductionist explanation of ethics. He considers that ethical concepts are pseudo-concepts and hence unanalysable. In other words, they are meaningless and when spoken, merely serve to show that their expression is attended by certain feelings in the speaker. In Ayer's opinion, ethical judgements have no validity whatever. Looked at from an individualistic viewpoint his argument has credibility, but with respect to society overall, it is, I believe, insufficient.

The validity of mathematics to describe many aspects of the universe is beyond question and, so it seems, is that of ethics in understanding social behaviour. Ethical values are similar in all the mainstream religions. Whether ethics led to religion or the other way round is an open question. The fact is that religious ethical laws or commandments form the basis of society and a reductionist explanation of them, from a logical positivist point of view, appears rather unsatisfactory. There is an underlying circularity in the reductionist argument. If they have no common objective value, then why should we care if people do not abide by them? Nevertheless, we do care a great deal about unethical behaviour. Matt Ridley in his book *The Origins of Virtue* writes:

> 'None the less the new gene-tilitarian understanding of human instincts that this book has explored leads to a few simple precepts for avoiding mistakes. Human beings have some instincts that foster the greater good and others that foster self interested and anti-social behaviour. We must design a society that encourages the former and discourages the latter.'

Firstly, what does he mean by mistakes? From a reductionist point of view, individuals make mistakes. As long as I do not make a mistake, why should I care if others make them?

Secondly, why should we design a society that encourages the greater good rather than one that encourages self-interest and anti-social behaviour? From a survival point of view, the former would benefit the weaker members of society while the latter would benefit the stronger. Without some forms of objective ethical values, why should the stronger care what happens to the weaker? Yet, the majority of mankind would agree with Ridley's statement. This, I maintain, admits some form of objectivity to ethical values, possibly, like mathematics, etched into an intersecting non-physical universe. I must emphasise that this is not an argument for the concept of an overall Creator. We do not really have enough evidence to argue in favour of such a concept. Nevertheless, we can deduce by the use of common sense that the ethics derived from religion in general have a practical validity even if the religions themselves are invalid in other respects. This implies that, when in Plato's *Republic*, Thrasymachus states that 'justice is the will of the stronger', he is wrong in principle. Justice is found in the ethical behaviour of human beings in society. This would be the case even if the reductionist argument were true.

We also know for sure that the universe is a source of conflict. For example, on earth there is unending conflict and competition within the animal kingdom, leading to a great deal of suffering and agony. If we adopt the Copernican Principle, it would seem that similar kinds of conflicts are likely to exist on other life-bearing planets. It appears that conflict is the inevitable result of biological evolution. It is also one of the factors leading to evolutionary progress with respect to efficiency. Unfortunately, too much and too violent conflict can lead to destruction and extinction. Hence the evolution of reciprocity and hence the human ethical calling to limit conflict to peaceful competition. Whether such competition is a reflection of a wider conflict within a parallel universe affecting our consciousness is a matter for debate, but it is a concept worth entertaining.

The Necessity of Ethical Foundations

Although the Copernican Principle appears to invalidate specific anthropomorphic religions, especially the fundamentalist versions of Judaism Christianity and Islam, their ethical foundations have been necessary for the formulation of behavioural boundaries in human society. The prohibition of theft and murder, for instance, common to all major religions, creates the conditions required for social harmony. In spite of wars, massacres and other enormities, such ethical principles have rendered possible the advance of civilisation, at least in terms of creativity and intellectual progress. Is it then possible to posit ethics in a secular society? I see no reason why not. After all, religion in its narrower interpretations has itself been a source of fierce conflict.

The argument for Theism seems to have been irretrievably lost by the establishment of the Copernican Principle. There is no hard scientific evidence whatsoever for any intervention by God in human affairs or even in natural processes. 'The sun shines and the rain falls upon the just and the unjust alike.' (St Matthew 5: 45) The argument for Deism is still a matter of debate. The argument for design, (see Chapter Four) first broached by William Paley, but later adapted to the ideas of modern cosmology, has not been fully countered. The idea of a parallel universe of unknown structure but whose boundary with our own universe is universal consciousness is at least as cosmologically respectable as Everett's 'Many Worlds' theory. This might or might not include the deistic concept.

From the purely scientific viewpoint, a very curious situation exists. The incredible number of apparent coincidences in the laws of physics that are necessary to account for the formation of life would seem to point to a Designer concept. The necessity to confine such parameters to certain values to produce living observers shows that initial manipulation of some sort would be necessary. A truly omnipotent Creator would have no need of manipulation. He could produce living observers directly, or in any manner that He wished. Either living beings are not his main concern, or such a Creator would not seem to be truly omnipotent, labouring under certain constraints (possibly self-imposed) determined by the laws of physics and mathematics (see Chapter Four). Although free to choose various physical parameters, He finds that the basic structure of physical reality appears to possess an independent existence. Such a Designer would certainly need to be omniscient, or almost omniscient. This curious situation led to Harrison's speculation that such a Designer is in fact a superior civilisation rather than an omnipotent God. A dualistic interpretation of events would also place constraints upon the Creator. After all, dualism posits the existence of an evil power challenging all the virtues of the Creator and one cannot persuasively challenge the omnipotent.

Under certain circumstances, the multi-universe theories could dispense with the idea of a Creator but not with the explanatory mathematics that appear to be indelibly etched into our universe. In addition, both ethics and aesthetics would appear to be similarly ensconced. It is significant that at least two highly ethical religions, Jainism and Buddhism, are atheistic. They do uphold the idea of reincarnation, for which there is no scientific evidence whatever. There is not even a theory of the mechanism for such a phenomenon. This is an additional reason why modern cosmology has little impact on the Eastern religions. It is difficult to contradict something for which there is not even a theoretical basis. The Copernican Principle does not contradict reincarnation, since not being anthropocentric; it could easily apply throughout the universe, finite or infinite.

The existence of a non-physical universe, intersecting our own through consciousness and possibly being the basis of the phenomenon of the self-organisation of matter, does not necessarily lead to a Designer. It could be that certain unknown aspects of the non-physical universe could dictate the parameters in our own universe to take values for the development of life-forms, making our universe a necessary result rather than a contingent entity.

Epilogue

My own view is, first, that the universe is orderly. Events occur according to the laws of physics and mathematics. We cannot prove that tomorrow, gravitational attraction will not suddenly change to gravitational repulsion or that the speed of light will not suddenly halve. Nevertheless, I do not believe that the universe is such an arbitrary construction.

Such considerations could support the Deistic argument, but it seems to rule out the concept of the resurrection in a new earth and a new heaven, as a specific event in space-time, rather than transcendent imagery. The arbitrary changes in the laws of physics, and hence biology, necessary for the bodily resurrection of the dead completely contradict the idea of an orderly physical universe. With modern technology however, we could introduce a 'Messianic' age of peace and plenty now, if we effected the necessary sociological transformation.

In their book, *The Moral Nature of the Universe*, Murphy and Ellis discuss the kenotic method of transforming society. Kenosis is a term originally applied by Christianity to the renunciation of divinity by God, in order to invest in the full humanity of Jesus. More generally, it denotes the deliberate sacrifice of personal advantage to advance the cause of humanity as a whole. This leads to the advocacy of non-violence as a means of resolving conflict. Murphy and Ellis put this forward as a Christian (Anabaptist/Quaker) ethic corresponding to the crucifixion. Alternatively, it also corresponds to a further development of the principle of TIT FOR TAT described in the last chapter. This would invoke the use of non-violence selectively, since certainty of reaction can sometimes lead to unnecessary exploitation and frustration.

The Moral Nature of the Universe goes into great detail regarding both the bottom-up argument from physics to design to ethics to theology, and the reverse top-down argument from God to ethics to design to teleology and sociology. The authors designate the overall form as a cumulative case argument. Although no single piece of evidence carries much weight in itself, the combined force of all the pieces is increased, because each piece increases the probability of every other piece. God is understood as a non-coercive agent responsible for the creation of free and intelligent beings in the universe. Free will gives them the opportunity to make ethical choices without external compulsion. The best choice would be to follow the example of God and use persuasion rather than coercion in dealings with their fellows, hence the advocacy of non-violence. Although the book has a Christian bias, the arguments and explanations they give could easily refer to a purely Deistic context, embracing the universe as a whole. There is no insistence upon belief in the incarnation or the resurrection as a necessity for salvation. According to the Anabaptist tradition, as opposed to Augustinian dualism, redemption comes through self-denial that includes suffering and non-violence even to the point of abjuring self-defence (*The Moral Nature of the Universe*, p250). Several Anabaptist writers would extend the principle of redemption through suffering, to include all living things in the universe. Holmes Rolston considers that suffering in the natural world is a necessary by-product of the features of life that promote the emergence of something higher. To quote from *The Moral Nature of the Universe*, p211:

> 'The whole natural history is somehow contained in God, God's doing, and that includes even suffering.'

It is interesting to compare this idea with the quotation from Chapter Seven (Isaiah 45:7),

> 'I form the light and create darkness: I make peace and create evil: I the Lord do all these things.'

This gives a pantheistic aspect of creation that would include Christianity, at least on this planet, as a moral harbinger of the kenotic ideal.

The whole concept of the necessity of the universe in all its variety, energy and suffering has a great deal in common with progressive Judaism which looks upon God as the guide to a universe of justice and compassion for all creatures. In this respect it could apply to all creation, however many life-bearing planets there are in the universe.

Murphy and Ellis have certainly given a logical and concise scientific account of the morality of the universe, with their claim to provide the missing metaphysical layer of theology essential to a full understanding of cosmology, containing the idea of kenosis as the central theme. This does seem to put limitations upon God's omnipotence, since the necessity of a physical universe evolving free will, appears to make suffering and evil an endemic part of existence, both for the universe and for God himself, if we are to fulfil the kenotic ideal. On the other hand, Ellis in his book *Before the Beginning*, claims that our universe is 'the simplest in hypothesis and richest in phenomena' for such a development, echoing Leibniz 'that this is the best of all possible worlds' – a claim that is rather difficult to substantiate, since we have no other universe with which to make a comparison.

As we have seen in Chapter Nine, not all religions agree with this final step in the hierarchy. Buddhism for example, accepts the objectivity of ethics in the four noble truths and the eightfold path to freedom without the concept of God as a higher being. In the eightfold path, one can easily discern the kenotic ideal emphasised by Murphy and Ellis.

Personally, I would concede the scientific basis of morality. Indeed, I think it possible to extend the Copernican principle to all the values postulated in a Platonic, intersecting non-physical universe. In other words, the same ethical and aesthetic values, in their broadest sense, would prevail throughout the physical universe wherever free-willed intelligent beings exist. I find the final hierarchical step towards a divine presence possible but difficult. It is much easier to consider it in pantheistic terms than in the interventionist concepts of the main Western Religions. Divine intervention in the universe, at the quantum level or otherwise, is from the scientific point of view, a non-sequitur.

I consider that the key to many of these deep and difficult questions of existence lies in the understanding of our own consciousness. So far, we have not even touched on a solution to this. Although we are beginning to comprehend the neurological working of the brain, the mystery of how unconscious matter can produce consciousness and identity is as puzzling as ever.

I put forward the idea of a parallel non-physical universe, as the source of consciousness and abstract values, as a basis for discussion. Perhaps some of the concepts of eastern mysticism combined with neurological scientific research can at least bring us a little nearer to a solution. The scientific method, based as it is upon statistics and measurement, may have its drawbacks; but it is all we have in our attempt to verify objective truth. One thing I feel strongly about is that the universe and everything therein and pertaining to it, including religion and mysticism, is eligible for the scientific method of investigation. I am at one with our mother Eve when she committed the 'happy sin' and ate the fruit of the Tree of Life.

I conclude with two well-known quotations with cosmological implications.

'Ah Love! Could thou and I with Fate conspire
To grasp this sorry Scheme of Things entire,
Would not we shatter it to bits - and then
Re-mould it nearer to the Heart's Desire!

The Rubaiyat of Omar Khayyam, Quatrain 73,
translated by Edward Fitzgerald.

Or alternatively...

'It is a tale
Told by an idiot, full of sound and fury
Signifying nothing.'

Shakespeare, *Macbeth, Act 5, Scene 5*

Appendix

Responses by Religious Authorities

The template of a letter to the following religious authorities

The Chief Rabbi

The Bishop of London

The Rev Dr Russell Stannard, Anglican Priest, Scientist and Author

The Rev Dr John Polkinghorne, Anglican Priest, Scientist and Author

The Rabbi of the Liberal Jewish Synagogue, St John's Wood, London

The Rabbi Emeritus of the Liberal Jewish Synagogue, St John's Wood London

A chaplain of Newmon House, Catholic Chaplaincy to the University of London

Dr P E Hodgson, Corpus Christi College, Oxford

Dear Rev or Rabbi, etc

I am writing a book on the effect of cosmology upon religion and I would be grateful for your comments on the following points.

As an important representative in this country of a pre-Copernican religion, does the established vastness of such a universe have any effect upon your belief or philosophy?

For example, the Hubble space telescope has determined the number of galaxies in the observable universe to be approximately fifty billion. This is about fifty times greater than previous estimates from ground-based telescopes. The number that we cannot observe either in principle or practice could be many times greater than that, even infinite, if the universe is an open structure. If we consider that our galaxy contains two hundred billion stars of which about ten per cent are sun-like stars, then twenty billion stars have, or have had, the possibility of possessing life-forming planetary systems. Even if this only applies to one in a million, that still leaves twenty thousand life-bearing planetary systems of which at least one has an advanced civilisation on it. It seems not unreasonable therefore to assume that each galaxy could contain at least one advanced civilisation.

Should this induce in us a certain amount of humility when we refer to Israel as God's chosen people (*and to Jesus Christ as redeeming all Christians into the "New Israel"? The Son of God sent to 'mankind' to cleanse them of their sins through acceptance and repentance. Christians are urged to spread the 'Good News' to mankind.*) *Because the Bible is a pre-Copernican document, 'mankind' refers to the then known inhabited universe, which consisted of our world alone. Should this now be extended to the fifty billion or so possible civilisations in the observable modern universe? (*If so then Christian proselytisers have quite a job on their hands*). *

A further point of interest lies in the now established age of the earth of about four billion years. For about two to three billion of those years, life on earth consisted of primitive forms of prokaryotic cell before life-forms that are more complex evolved culminating in ourselves. At what stage in this process did the soul of man become manifest? Alternatively, do all living things have some kind of soul? I would be most interested to know your views on this subject.

Following this, is a certain amount of flexibility allowed in interpretation of the Bible with respect to the discoveries of modern science?

Your thoughts on these matters would be most valuable to me as a scientist and (rather sceptical) student of the Bible. It would also be of great help if they could be included in my projected book on the subject.

Yours sincerely,

Adair Butchins

* Included in letters to Christian authorities

Replies

1 Rabbi Dr Jonathon Sacks, the Chief Rabbi

1st April 1998

Dear Dr Butchins,

The Chief Rabbi has asked me to respond on his behalf to your letter of the 16th of December 1997.

I am sorry that it has taken so long to get back to you; the sheer volume of work in the Chief Rabbi's office has made it impossible for me to do so until now. You have asked a number of important questions and I will try to answer them as best I can.

The Jewish tradition has always seen the universe as being extraordinarily vast. It is its apparent limitlessness, in contrast to our relative puniness, which, for many Jewish thinkers, has traditionally served as a reminder of the need for humility and awe in the face of God and his creation. Therefore the discovery of billions of more galaxies is not a theological problem. On the contrary, it is further proof of the awesome power of the Creator.

The idea that there may well be life elsewhere in the universe does not in any way pose a problem for us today; to put it simply – we'll cross that bridge if and when we come to it.

Jews have always understood the creation story in the book of Genesis as being one of the most esoteric sections of the Bible, and have never read it in a simplistic way.

There is a tremendous amount of exegetical material which attempts to interpret the Creation story in the light of scientific progress, much of it very successful and compelling. May I suggest the book *Genesis and the Big Bang* by Gerald Schroeder, which should be available at any Jewish bookstore.

I hope this has been of help.

Yours sincerely

Rabbi Shimon Felix

Note: Gerald Schroeder's books, *Genesis and the Big Bang* and *The Science of God,* are discussed in Chapter Six, The Anthropic Principle.

2 The Rt. Rev and Rt Hon Richard Chartres The Bishop of London

8th February 2000

Dear Dr Butchins

Thank you for your letter about cosmology and religion.

Your letter deserves a fuller answer than I have leisure to give but doubtless you will have already read the many treatments of this subject. I found Paul Davies *God and the New Physics* particularly helpful and challenging. It may be worth pointing out, however, that the discoveries of Copernicus neither invalidate the wisdom of Corinthians 13 nor have they prevented the rise of post-Copernican religious movements like Nazism.

The scandal of particularity to which you refer, has always been a scandal that the communication of God should come through a particular person in a small town in an obscure corner of a world empire. The humility and vulnerability of God is indeed one of the most astonishing aspects of the revelation expressed through Jesus Christ.

You talk about flexibility in hermeneutics. In your researches into the Church Fathers, you will certainly have discovered creativity in their dialogue with the biblical tradition that is light years away from fundamentalism. Fundamentalism of the sort that you rightly deride is in fact a rather recent phenomenon and an unwilling tribute to the false move that we have made philosophically, in restricting the concept of truth to what can be established by number-based measurements of one kind or another.

I am thrilled by the new matter for praise and thanksgiving that has been revealed by microscope and telescope. I do think that there is a huge artistic challenge that remains ungrasped by Christian poets and artists. Our ideas of God are too small. That is perhaps why the word of God came not in the form of a philosophical tract but in the person of one who lived a life of self-sacrifice and who found fullness of life by passing through non-entity. In my experience, these are truths which cannot be proved or disproved but you can be convinced to the extent to which you love your neighbour indefatigably. To the extent to which you grow in this love you become certain of the reality of God and the immortality of your own soul This rather than any mere cerebral or mental gyrations is the way the saints have followed.

Yours sincerely

The Rt Rev and Rt Hon Richard Chartres

3 The Rev Dr Russell Stannard, Anglican Priest, Scientist and Author

Physics Department
The Open University
Walton Hall
Milton Keynes MK7 6AA

30th November 2000

Dear Dr Butchins

Thank you for your letter of the 19th November asking for my views on many questions. The issues you raised are deep ones and can only be answered adequately at length. I never like dashing off some hurried response in letter-form because such replies never do justice to what I really think.

The best I can do is to refer you to the book based on my Gilford lectures: *The God Experiment*, published in paperback by Faber and Faber. Much of that book is devoted to exploring my views about the way cosmology and astronomy impinge on religious belief and our understanding of the status of human beings in the overall scheme of things. You are of course at liberty to quote any thing of interest in that book, with the appropriate acknowledgement. I hope you will find that book of some interest.

You might also like to know that I recently edited a book *God for the 21st Century* (SPCK) in which are set forth the views of fifty scientists on a whole range of issues at the interface of religion and science – many touching on cosmology.

Best wishes

Russell Stannard

4. The Rev Dr John Polkinghorne, Anglican Priest, Scientist and Author

74 Hurst Park Avenue
Cambridge CB4 2AF

6th December 2000

Dear Dr Butchins

I returned from the USA yesterday to find your letter asking a good many interesting questions. Here are some thoughts:

There must be many potential sites in the universe for the evolution of life but we do not know how easy it is for this to happen. Therefore, it is scientifically uncertain whether there is extra-terrestrial life or not. Theologically the matter has been debated since the seventeenth century when Galileo's discovery that the moon and the planets are made of the same stuff as earth put the question of Martians, etc on the agenda. My view would be that we should be wary of setting limits to the fertility of God's creation. If there are 'little green men' out there, God will care for them as for all creatures and if they need redemption, I believe that the Word will have taken little green flesh just as he did our flesh. Some theologians, however, believe that it would have been sufficient for the Word to have become a creature somewhere to redeem all creatures.

For my views on the nature of the soul see chapter 9 of my *Science and Christian Belief* (SPCK). As for the Bible: truth is one, and the theological truths of scripture (but not the incidental contemporary language its human

219

writers necessarily used) and the truths of science must be compatible with each other, though we may have some struggles in seeing exactly what this involves. Each can illuminate the other. This is a point of view at least as old as St Augustine.

Yours sincerely
J Polkinghorne

Note: Russell Stannard and John Polkinghorne's books, *The God Experiment* and *Science and Christian Belief*, are discussed below.

These two Christian apologists, Russell Stannard and John Polkinghorne, have recently published books based upon their Gifford lectures, given at Aberdeen University from 1993 to 1998. In his will, Lord Gifford required the lectures to promote, advance, teach and diffuse the study of Natural Theology and to treat it as a strictly natural science, like astronomy or chemistry. Both of these authors are theoretical elementary particle physicists and Anglican Priests. Russell Stannard's book *The God Experiment* is addressed to the general public, while Polkinghorne's *Science and Christian Belief* is written from a more esoteric standpoint.

The God Experiment is an attempt to establish belief in God and hence Christianity, in the form of an experimental endeavour. Since Stannard is an Anglican priest, he labours under the same restriction that applies to the work of Willem Drees. The result of the 'experiment' is known beforehand. This is reasonable enough, except that the word experiment is a misnomer; it is a demonstration rather than an experiment.

The book commences with a description of a 'prayer experiment' – taking place in the United States. 1,200 heart-surgery patients are divided into two groups. Only one group will be prayed for by special teams of intercessors drawn from a variety of religious denominations. The patients themselves will not know to which group they belong.

Over a period of two to three years, their case histories will be studied to see if there is any difference between the recovery rates of the two groups. It is claimed that the project has been designed as a strictly controlled scientific experiment.

Stannard himself admits that there are too many unknown and unquantified factors involved to qualify it as an attempt to discover anything about God. It seems more like superstitious rigmarole than a scientific experiment.

After this introduction, the book gives a very erudite exposition of the case for Theism. As a scientist, he accepts the general scientific consensus on evolution and cosmology. As a Theist, he makes a perceptive comparison between genetic inheritance and original sin. On the subject of miracles and God's intervention, he uses biblical interpretation, since there are no scientifically hard facts available. He concludes that miracles are 'not intrinsically impossible'.

Like Penrose, he looks at consciousness and free will from the point of view of particle physics.

On the problem of evil and suffering, he is on rather shaky ground. After a discourse on the problem he concludes 'that in the final analysis suffering is beyond understanding; it is something we must bear patiently trusting that the loving all-powerful God will in his own time and in his own way, ensure that all will be well'.

It is beyond understanding only if we believe in this loving omnipotent God. There are other solutions, as we can see in Chapter Seven.

The highly improbable series of events and conditions necessary for the formation of life in a contingent universe is considered as evidence for an intelligent Creator. The multi-universe solution is dismissed as contravening Ockham's Razor (see Chapter One, Realists and Nominalists), although why an intelligent supernatural Creator is the simpler solution is not made clear. Theology, after all, is just as complicated and speculative a subject as cosmology.

As far as Christianity is concerned, both Stannard and Polkinghorne make the astonishing assertion that the 'Son of God' could be incarnate on each planet containing intelligent alien life. This is astonishing because the whole basis of Christianity is the fact that Jesus Christ is the one and only saviour. To quote the Creed:

> 'I believe in God the Father almighty,
> Maker of Heaven and earth,
> And in Jesus Christ, His *only* Son our Lord.'

Presumably, the assertion is made because of the impossibility of any communication with planets in the distant regions of space-time. This problem, however, presented itself long before the Copernican revolution. The same could have been said of the distant regions and times of our own planet. A similar argument about the second coming was why St Augustine considered the Antipodes uninhabited (see Chapter Two, A Historic Analogy). Nowhere has it been suggested that there were further incarnations of God in flesh. Such an idea in ancient times could easily have invoked the charge of heresy. It is just as well that the inquisition is defunct.

Stannard has the original idea that the human spirit evolved in compass with the human body. At first sight, this seems at odds with evolutionary theory because it appears to have no survival value. If we consider that such spirituality is implicitly integrated with free will, however, then the very distinctive survival value of free will (see Chapter Two, Free Will) would ensure the evolution of the spirit, although the existence of it is not generally recognised by most modern biologists.

Russell Stannard has written an absorbing and important book with many original insights into the nature of religion and Christianity in conformity with the scientific outlook.

Polkinghorne's book, *Science and Christian Belief* is much more theological than *The God Experiment*. It is concerned mainly with the exposition of Trinitarian Christian belief, built upon the Deistic premise. Polkinghorne rejects an obscurantist incorrigible picture of religious belief. As a scientist, he refers to Natural Theology (knowledge of God through empiricism) as an essential input to theological inquiry.

He compares the mystery of the incarnation in Christ with the mystery of superposition and wave-particle duality in quantum physics, not as an explanation but as an analogy.

He gives a very learned dissertation upon the crucifixion and resurrection of Jesus. He expounds upon the survival of Christianity after the apparent defeat and execution of Jesus. The disheartened and dispirited disciples could only have been revitalised and re-energised by the remarkable event of the resurrection of Christ. This assumption depends upon a reading of the Gospels, but the survival of Christianity is incontrovertible. Sceptics put its survival down to the conversion of Constantine in AD312, more for political than religious purposes. It certainly explains why the Jews rather than the Romans were deemed guilty of Deicide. It does not explain the survival of Christianity for its first three hundred years although the exceptional organising ability of St Paul must have created the necessary conditions of hope and expectation.

Like Stannard, Polkinghorne considers that the intransigent mystery of evil defies our theological understanding. The idea of a dualistic explanation is not mentioned. In fact, Satan is completely ignored, in spite of his important place in Christian theology.

The chapter on eschatology is possibly the most interesting. Polkinghorne accepts the scientific projections for the future of our universe – either the heat death or the big crunch. Nevertheless, he considers that in due course God will completely refashion the universe to accord with the prophetic vision of a 'New earth and a New Heaven'; the resurrection of Christ being the forerunner of the resurrection of all. This is an absorbing thought, but if Tippler's ideas read like science fiction, Polkinghorne's eschatology reads like science fantasy. This is not, necessarily, to preclude its validity. After all, a non-physical universe has already been postulated to explain the phenomena of consciousness and self-organisation (see Chapter Eight).

Science and Christian Belief is not an easy read. It appears to be aimed at theologians, or at least, at people with a fair understanding of the technicalities of theology. Its arguments are lucid and persuasive and amply repay the concentration needed for its perusal.

5 Rabbi Dr David Goldberg
The Rabbi of the Liberal Jewish Synagogue

St John's Wood, London

10th February 2000

Dear Adair

Thank you for your letter of 2nd February. You ask me if my beliefs and philosophy as a Progressive Jew are affected by post-Copernican discoveries about the nature of the universe. The answer is, of course, 'yes'. It is only a fundamentalist (i.e. someone who regards the Torah as literally the word of God which cannot therefore be modified or changed in any way) who would seek to maintain a pre-Copernican cosmology in the modem world. Our views on the creative process must, therefore, take into account the findings of modern science and ancillary disciplines.

Your question about the chosen people is, if I may say so, somewhat confused. I have no doubt that the ancient Hebrews believed that they were indeed 'chosen by God' as did the first Christians with their 'new' testament, and Mohammed's followers who believed he was Allah's one true prophet. In other words, every ancient religion sought to justify itself as being God's specially chosen representative. To say that the Jews were 'chosen to bring to mankind the knowledge of the one true God' is to offer a rabbinic Midrash on that concept; that is to say, it is an attempt to interpret and modify the starkness of the statement that God is only interested in the Jews. In the same way, Christianity and Islam have to incorporate in their theologies an awareness of other people created in the divine image, but who did not subscribe to Christianity or Islam.

In so far as I have read and understood physics, I readily accept the notion that the world is about four billion years old. The question as to at what stage in the process of development 'soul' appears is not a valid one. That is to say, the concept of a soul is a theological and philosophical idea to express the notion that humankind is not solely corporeal and that there is more to life than our few short years here on earth. The ancient Greek philosophers, the Jewish prophets and the rabbis, the gurus of the eastern religions all struggle to find some comfort for the otherwise terrible notion that we exist briefly for no more significant purpose.

The metaphysical notion of a soul obviously cannot be incorporated into a material explanation of what constitutes a human being. You must allow it as a religious or poetic metaphor that has brought comfort to us over the millennia as we struggle to give meaning to the existential uncertainties of our brief lives. Cease to be a scientist and become a philosopher for a few minutes while you absorb this fact that cannot be substantiated by telescopes!

With fondest regards to you and Janet and please come back to me if my answers do not satisfy you or require further amplification.

As ever,

David J Goldberg

6 Rabbi Dr John Rayner
Rabbi Emeritus of the Liberal Jewish Synagogue

St John's Wood
London

2nd February 2000

Dear Dr Butchins,

Thank you for your letter of 2nd February. It was a pleasure to see you at the Synagogue the other day; also to read your article in the *Jewish Chronicle*. Do please continue to refute the fundamentalists as and when necessary – they must not be allowed to get away with it. (In that connection, the enclosed pamphlet might interest you.)

I am very glad that you are writing a book on the effect of cosmology on religion and shall be immensely interested in what your research uncovers. My impression is that it has been considered only (a) by fundamentalists, in a vain attempt to refute it, and (b) by the more radical and philosophically minded theologians. Among the latter, on the Jewish side, there are probably some interesting comments on the subject you raise to be found in the writings of, e.g. Louis Jacobs, Eugene Borowitz, Emil Fackenheim, Richard Rubenstein, etc., and when I have a little more time than at present I will look up what they have to say.

Also, if you would like me to write something sufficiently well considered to be quotable for possible inclusion in your book, please let me know roughly how long it should be and by what date it would be required.

Meanwhile I can only give you and off-the-cuff response. In brief it would be that the new cosmological discoveries which in essence though not in scale have been 'around' all my adult life have not seemed to me in the least to invalidate my religious beliefs, if only because I have always taken them into account.

Clearly, they refute a fundamentalist reading of the early chapters of Genesis but of course Liberal Judaism has never taken that view; on the contrary, the rejection of it may be said to be its chief defining characteristic. More precisely, I regard the first eleven chapters of Genesis as purely mythological and not historical at all and in particular as a re-working of still older Mesopotamian creation myths (such as Gilgamesh, probably going back to the 3rd millennium BCE) from a Hebraic point of view but without completely eradicating pre-Hebraic and pre-monotheistic motifs.

Even apart from these opening chapters, it is clear that the entire Bible was written from a pre-Copernican, geocentric, anthropocentric and indeed Judeo-centric point of view which, in these respects, is at variance with modern knowledge.

The greater the universe, the greater its Creator. And if there are living beings elsewhere in the Universe, which is clearly possible and perhaps probable though less than certain, then these are under the dominion of the One God, who is indeed referred to in the Jewish liturgy as 'The Source of the Life of All Worlds'.

Does it mean that we must reject the belief that God takes an interest in human life on Planet earth? Not at all. Logically, it is possible that God may take an interest in all forms of intelligent life, even if that exists in an infinite number of places.

Does it mean that Judaism's ethical principles lack universal validity? I don't think so. I think that genuine ethical principles are by definition universal and, like logical principles, hold true 'in all possible worlds'. Therefore, if it were alleged that in some other world there operates, with divine approval, an ethical code by which falsehood is preferable to truth, hatred to love, contempt for life to respect for life, etc., I would reject that allegation.

Do we have to reject the concept of man as 'the Crown of Creation'? No, we only have to add: in the corner of the universe that we inhabit.

As regards the Chosen People concept that needs to be considerably 'toned down' (as it is in our Liberal Jewish liturgy), quite apart from the new cosmology, in the light of what we now know about other religions. But I don't think it needs to be rejected altogether. It is only necessary to restate it by saying that Judaism has a unique contribution to make to the religious thought and life of humanity on Planet Earth.

I am afraid that is the best I can do at the moment; perhaps it is of some slight use as a first shot.

All good wishes,

Rabbi John D. Rayner

7 A reply to my letter from a Chaplain of Newman House, the Catholic Chaplaincy to the Universities of London

16th March 2001

First, he insists that these are his personal views rather than the *Official Doctrine* of the Catholic Church, although it seems to me that to produce an *Official Doctrine* on such subjective matters would be difficult.

He then describes a sense of wonder at the vastness of the universe and of awe and reverence for its Creator. He claims not to rule out the existence of alien civilisations but insists that if such beings are in need of redemption, then this will be offered them through the person of God the Son who assumed mankind's nature, in the same way as it extends to mankind at all times and in all places. Such redemption, therefore, is not limited by space-time.

It is impossible to date the first moment when God created and infused the first rational soul into a body, which may have evolved for such a union (see the section on Free Will and the evolution of the Spirit in the review of Russell Stannard's book *The God Experiment* in this appendix). The presence of such a soul is manifest in the specific human activities of understanding and willing.

All living creatures have a soul but the human soul is also spiritual and subsistent, capable of existing even when separated from the body. Human consciousness is an activity flowing from the essence of each unique rational soul possessed by the individual person.

The truths revealed to us for our salvation are not contradicted by either historical or scientific evidence.

They are revealed by means of the human authors of the scriptures under the inspiration of the Holy Spirit.

Truth can be expressed in many ways other than through the empirical disciplines of science and history.

The letter concludes with the wish that these reflections may be of some use to the subject of this book.

Note: It is pleasing to note that this letter is neither obscurantist nor dogmatic, but adopts a completely logical stance to the mystery of the universe as opposed to the fundamentalist view often prevalent in all religions and denominations.

8   *From Dr P E Hodgson*

Corpus Christie College
Oxford OX1 4JF

Dear Dr Butchins

Thanks for your letter of 20th March. Enclosed is a lecture that may go some way to answer your questions. (The Second Coyne Lecture on Theology and Science, Pontifical Academy of Theology, Cracow, Poland, 21st March 1995, Corpus Christie College, Oxford)

My specific answers to your questions are:

The vastness of the universe increases our awe at the power of God.

I will consider alien civilisations when their existence is demonstrated. The figures you give for the number of other civilisations are completely hypothetical.

Do you have any evidence to support your postulated parallel universe?

The Bible exists to teach us the way to save our souls, not to teach science. If anything is definitely established by science, then the Bible has to be interpreted accordingly. The truth of the Bible is guaranteed by the authority of the Church, and the Church can give an authoritative interpretation. This is carefully explained in many books.

You may recall that Copernicus (a canon), Galileo, Lemaitre (priest) and very many Jesuit astronomers through the last three hundred years, were all Catholics.

You may quote my views, and I will be glad to elaborate them if need be.

With best wishes for your project,

Yours sincerely

P. E. Hodgson

NOTES

The evidence for the existence of a parallel universe is discussed in Chapter Eight, Consciousness.

The figures given for the existence of other civilisations are based upon a very conservative statistical analysis (see Drake's equation, Chapter Two).

To quote from the Journal of the Royal Astronomical Society, *Astronomy and Geophysics:* February 2001 Vol 42 Issue 1 p.17:

'So far, about fifty stars within about 200 light years from the earth have been catalogued with an orbiting companion. Experience on earth suggests that elementary life is hardy and will begin whenever and wherever it can. It survives in extreme circumstances of hot and cold and under high and low pressures. The chemical composition involves the normal chemical elements common throughout the galaxy. This leads one to accept as a reasonable hypothesis the possibility that such life exists elsewhere, although there is yet no hard evidence that this might be so.

Advanced living material requires more stringent conditions. It is generally agreed to need a solid planet located in the broad temperature range 0.07-1.60 AU from a solar type star. Liquid water is essential if our experience on earth is generally valid. The planetary orbit must be stable and significant surface impacts must be extremely rare. This implies the existence of at least one Jupiter mass in an exterior orbit of very low eccentricity to act as a trap for stray bodies. How large the semi-major axis must be is not clear, but we may require 2.0 AU as a minimum. There are requirements of the solid planet as well. It must be sufficiently massive to retain an atmosphere over cosmic periods. This will filter harmful radiation. The planet must not be too massive however, because it is difficult for bone to withstand falls in very large gravity and the energy required for movement becomes very large in such cases.

The question then is, whether any of the systems observed so far could begin to satisfy these conditions? Excluding systems with very small values of the semi-major axis, we are left with four systems that might ultimately satisfy our criteria as being possible havens for advanced life. The three systems, 47 Uma, HD 10697 and e Eridani (the nearest star to earth so far discovered to have an orbiting companion) Have the required minimum semi-major axis. The system u Andromeda is more complex but could also fit our criteria.

This gives at least four systems capable of possibly harbouring advanced life forms within about 200 light years of earth. This on average would give, at this moment, about 250,000 candidates in our galaxy. One system per galaxy under the circumstances appears to be a very conservative estimate indeed.'

The template of a letter to Islamic religious authorities

7th March 2001

Dear Muslim Researchers,

I am writing a book on the effect of cosmology upon religion and I would be grateful for your comments on the following points.

As serious and knowledgeable scholars of a pre-Copernican religion in a post Copernican universe, does the vastness of such a universe have any effect upon your belief or philosophy?

What was the effect upon the Muslim world of the Copernican Heliocentric Theory as confirmed by Galileo? The Christian world was extremely disturbed and antithetical to this idea, but I am not sure of the Muslim reaction. Although, unlike Christianity, Islam recommends the study of scientific evidence, I presume, as in all religions, there were disputes among the contemporary philosophers.

What is the modern Islamic view, with respect to the existence of other alien civilisations within the universe?

The Hubble space telescope has determined the number of galaxies in the observable universe to be approximately fifty billion. This is about fifty times greater than previous estimates from ground based telescopes.

The number that we cannot observe, either in principle or practice, could be many times greater than that, even infinite, if the universe is an open structure. If we consider that our galaxy contains about two hundred billion stars of which about ten per cent are sun-like stars, then twenty billion stars have, or have had, the possibility of possessing life-forming planetary systems.

Even if this only applies to one in a million, that still leaves twenty thousand life-bearing planetary systems, of which at least one has an advanced civilisation on it. It seems not unreasonable, therefore, to assume that each galaxy could contain at least one advanced civilisation.

Should this induce in us a certain amount of humility when we refer to the Prophet Muhammad as the Master of Messengers? Chosen to bring to '*the pagans of mankind*' the knowledge of the one true God.

Since the Koran is a pre-Copernican document, '*mankind*' refers to the then known inhabited universe that consisted of our world alone. Should this now be extended to the fifty billion or so possible civilisations in the observable modern universe? If so, could there be such a Prophet for each civilisation in the universe?

A further point of interest lies in the established age of the earth of about four billion years. For about two to three billion of those years, life on earth consisted of primitive forms of prokaryotic cell before life-forms that are more complex evolved, culminating in ourselves. At what stage in this process did the soul of man become manifest? Or do all living things have some kind of soul? I would be most interested to know your views on this subject.

Leading on from this, is it still incumbent upon orthodox Muslims to believe in the Koran as the literal given word of God? Or is a certain amount of flexibility allowed in interpretation, with respect to the discoveries of modern science?

Your thoughts and opinions on these matters would be most valuable to me as a scientist and student of religion. They would also be of great help, if with your permission; I could quote them in my projected book on the subject.

I remain

Yours sincerely

Adair Butchins (Dr)

From Dr. Usama Hassan
Muslim Research Society

Dear Adair

Some of the questions you asked are, I feel symptomatic of modern man, and his way of looking at things. Most urban people have no idea of the beauty of the night sky, the constellation patterns or the movements of the planets. People are astounded when you point out to them, Jupiter, Venus, Saturn, Mars and Mercury. They only know these bodies from photographs or television. People have a 'view from outer space' of the solar system, the galaxies etc. thanks to film and photography, but very little idea of the original 'human-centric experience' of the universe, which is still accessible today. Many ancient civilisations had a deep understanding of this experience and were very reflective, seeing the image of the human soul in the vastness, harmony and order of the universe. The concept of 'fitra', denoting the original state of creation, includes such ideas.

It was only when I delved into observational astronomy over the last three years that I realised how inadequately the subject of astronomy/cosmology is taught at school and university. Despite an MA in Theoretical Physics from Cambridge and a PhD, I had virtually no idea of the breathtaking beauty of the movements of the heavenly bodies around us. Friends with PhDs in Physics or stellar astronomy have expressed the same disappointment. This is a key failing of the way science is taught in a non-sacred context.

As to some specific questions:

1 The heliocentric vs. the geocentric universe

Many Muslim scholars of the past held that the universe is geocentric and that the earth is flat. Many others who had studied the sciences disagreed, but there was no fundamental rift about it, because all agreed that the reflective content, the meaning of Allah's creation, the signs of Allah in His creation as well as in his revelation were more important.

For example, it is stated in the fifteenth-century commentary on the Koran, Tafsir al-Jalalayn: 'Most of the scholars of the law hold that the earth is flat, thus differing from the scholars of geometry who hold that it is spherical, although this issue does not contradict any fundamental principle of the sacred Law.'

Our contemporary Martin Lings (also known as Abu Bakr Siraj ad-Din) writes that the geocentric universe symbolises theomorphic man at the centre of creation made in God's image as the source of all existence; the heliocentric universe symbolises God as the source of existence directly, since the sun is a powerful symbol of the Light and Power of God. He thus argues that the difference in the two perspectives is not as great as is often made out.

The heliocentric theory was known to the Greeks and to pre-Copernican Muslim scholars. In fact, Copernicus was pre-empted in his models by the Muslim astronomers Muhammad al-Battani, Nasir al-Din al-Tusi and Ibn al-Shatir of Damascus. Refer to the chapter on Islamic astronomy in *The Cambridge Concise History of Astronomy*.

2 Life and prophets on other planets

I think that the idea of extraterrestrial intelligence has become the Holy Grail of modern astronomers without a shred of direct evidence. Modern western man is firmly convinced of its existence, the whole genre of sci-fi and alien films entrenches this in the public imagination. However the only basis for it, really, is the probability based arguments you indicated, where I think even the estimates of the order of magnitude of probabilities is subject to errors of orders of magnitude. However, as Islam inspired so much of western science, Muslims should prepare to accept real evidence either way. 'Say:

Bring your proof if you are truthful!' As per the Koranic expression.

With regard to a revelation-based perspective, there are certain statements in the Koran and Hadith (traditions of the deeds and sayings of the Prophet) that may or may not refer to extra-terrestrial life. Contemporary scholars have differing views on this. One example is the last verse of Surat al-Talaq (Divorce), which mentions that Allah has created seven heavens and 'of earth, a similar number'. This reference to the 'seven earths' possibly refers to other life-bearing planets. The number seven is often used in Arabic to denote 'many'. On this particular verse there are some intriguing statements from the Prophet's cousin Ibn Abbas, who is regarded as one of the foremost commentators on the Koran. These have been transmitted in the classical commentaries of Tabari and Ibn Kathir. The fullest version of the explanation is 'There are seven earths in each one of which, is a Prophet like your Prophet, an Adam like Adam, a Noah like Noah, an Abraham like Abraham, and a Jesus like Jesus'. This amazing statement is referring to extra-terrestrial life. It reminds me of parallel worlds in quantum physics! However, as a note of caution I have not been able to ascertain the authenticity of these reported sayings from a Hadith perspective.

The above would lead to the not-surprising conclusion that were there extra-terrestrial life, it would be provided with revelation by God and with its equivalent measure of Prophets. The status of our final Messenger remains undiminished. He would simply have counterparts in other worlds. Since Muslims believe in the Koranic assertion that every nation on this earth had a Prophet with essentially the same nature and message as other

Prophets, it is not such a wide extrapolation to include Prophets on other planets.

I hope this is of help

Usama Hasan

NOTES

I think the idea of teaching science in a sacred, but not necessarily a religious concept, would require both teacher and student to first have a grounding in the arts, especially the visual arts. This is desirable, but in most cases impractical, in modern educational practice. The onus is on the students themselves, to broaden the basis of their artistic knowledge and aesthetic appreciation.

It is interesting that in the fifteenth century, scholars of the law, who relied on authority, considered the earth flat while scholars of geometry who relied on evidence considered it spherical. See Chapter One, Under, Monotheism and the Greek Enlightenment.

Copernicus initiated the heliocentric theory because of doubts concerning the inconsistencies in the Ptolemaic astronomical model. Thabit ibn Qurra, a scholar from Baghdad, had expressed these doubt or 'shukuk' in the ninth century. They mainly concerned the retrograde motion of the planets and the difficulty of reconciling this motion with the Greek Aristotelian astronomical principle of constant motion in a circle. The three astronomers al-Battani, al-Tusi and al-Shatir refined the Ptolemaic methods and the geometrical devices used by al-Shatir were those used later by Copernicus. There seems to be no evidence that any of these Islamic astronomers envisaged a heliocentric universe. The only evidence I can find of an Islamic scholar examining such a possibility is al-Biruni in the tenth century. See Chapter One, under The Islamic Contention.

As regards quotations from the Koran regarding extra-terrestrial life, see Chapter Two, under The Displacement of Mankind and Religious Apologia.

To say that there is not a shred of evidence for extra-terrestrial intelligence is not altogether correct. There is the discovery of what are claimed to be fossils of bacterial life-forms, in a meteorite originating from Mars. If this were confirmed, then the separate formation of life on at least two planets in our solar system would give further confirmation of the Copernican Principle. We know that life itself is tenacious and ubiquitous on our own planet. There is no reason to believe that such is not the case throughout the universe. Statistically, the evolution of intelligent life on one planet per galaxy of two hundred billion stars does not seem far-fetched. Even if we take an error of magnitude a million times greater, one example per million galaxies would still leave about fifty thousand examples in the observable universe alone. See the Drake equation in Chapter Two, Under, The Probability of Extra-Terrestrial Civilisations. One thing that these statistics do indicate is that the chance of actually making contact with any such civilisation is almost negligible. It shows that the whole genre of sci-fi and alien films is pure fiction and never likely to be realised, because of the vastness of inter-galactic distances. See Chapter Two, under Life in the Universe.

The quotation from the Hadith is interesting. The Islamic religion has no problem with the idea of other Prophets on other planets. It does not have the exclusivity of the Orthodox Jewish and especially the mainstream Christian religions. It does embrace the concept of Judgement Day and Heaven and Hell, but many Muslims would describe them as transcendental imagery rather than intervention in the physical universe.

From Shoaib Qureshi
A Researcher at Philips

Just some thoughts off the top of my head

In the Koran God puts man in his place by comparing his creation with the universe.

Astronomical signs are presented as ordered, and therefore, importantly can be made use of by man.

Phenomena are described from man's point of observation (presumably so that we can relate to it).

The pre-decadence Muslims had a very dynamic approach to knowledge and experimentation as befitting people exploring the wonders of creation.

The Muslim world has never had the equivalent of an overbearing Church which spelt out a static order, which all must comply with.

Reason and observation have a pre-eminent place in the dynamic process of Islam. In this sense, Islam is unique. Islam is reasoned commitment, as opposed to commitment with reasons. The implication of this attitude to truth is that were it possible for the Muslim to find something more truthful he should adopt it. Muslims allow themselves to be challenged and will indeed change if what they discover is correct. This attitude of dedication to the 'truth' whatever it is should make a vibrant Islamic civilisation remarkably robust and agile.

NOTE

See Chapter Nine, under Islam (Submission to God).

Glossary

AGE OF THE SUN

The age of the sun is determined by calculations based upon its observed spectral chemical composition and its radiative energy output. This gives a present age of about five billion years, with about another five billion to go until its nuclear fuel is exhausted and it becomes a red giant star. In addition, the age of the earth, established by radioactive dating (see **Radioactive Dating**), is about four billion years, giving a good correspondence with the age of the sun.

ALGORITHM

A specific arithmetic procedure that will either accomplish some computing task in a finite time or report that it cannot do so.

ARIAN

A devotee of the Christian heresy of Arianism, promulgated in the fourth century by Arius. He maintained that Christ the Son was of different substance from God the Father, because the Son had a beginning while God is without beginning. Not to be confused with:

ARYAN

The name adopted by the East European invaders of Persia and India in about 3000 BC. They styled themselves Aryans, which means the nobility. They were responsible for the introduction of Zoroastrianism to the Indo-Iranian sub-continent. The name was subsequently taken up by the Nazi party in Germany to designate the non-Jewish population of Western Europe.

ASTRONOMICAL UNIT (AU)

Unit of distance used in the measurement of orbits and trajectories within the solar system. One AU is the average distance between the earth and the sun. Its value has been established as, roughly, 149,600,000 km (92,956,00 mi).

BIRTH SIGN

One of the twelve zodiacal constellations that the sun passes at the time of birth.

CLASSICAL COSMOLOGY

In classical general relativitistic cosmology, the underlying space-time (manifold) is fixed and unique events and positions are given with reference to it.

ECLIPTIC

The imaginary annual path of the sun around the earth, against the background of the constellations of the stars on an imaginary celestial stellar sphere. On its journey, the sun passes across the twelve constellations of the Zodiac.

EQUINOX

The projection of the equator onto the imaginary celestial stellar sphere.

EQUINOXES

The two points at which the ecliptic cuts the equinox, the ascending point being the First Point of Aries (spring) and the descending point being the First Point of Libra (autumn).

ELECTRIC DIPOLE MOMENTS

Two electrical charges that are large in comparison with their separation.

EMULATION

It is more than simulation. It should mimic exactly the behaviour of the circumstances that it is emulating.

EXPONENTIAL EXPANSION OF SPACE

As time increases by equal amounts, the volume of space is multiplied by equal amounts giving a very rapid expansion.

HIGGS FIELDS

The fields responsible for initiating the symmetry breaking of the unified force of the early universe to the four forces that we can discern now. They do this by first reducing the energy density to the false vacuum. Quantum tunnelling to the present energy density of the universe completes it.

ISOTROPY

Equal density in all directions

LOGICAL POSITIVISM

Unverifiable and untestable metaphysical propositions concerning the universe are without genuine meaning. Only scientifically verifiable knowledge concerning the contingent natural world of sense experience is valid.

MORAL IMPERATIVE

Sometimes known as the Categorical Imperative (Immanuel Kant). Act only according to the maxim by which you can, at the same time, will that it should become a universal law.

Doing that which is right irrespective of your desires.

NATURAL NUMBERS

The series 0, 1, 2, 3, 4, 5, 6.........n, n+1,....etc.

NON-SEQUITUR

A conclusion that does not follow from the evidence given.

NUMINOUS

Pertaining to the Divine.
Awe-inspiring.

PRECESSION OF THE EQUINOXES

The spinning earth is in fact a free gyroscope. The slightly distorted sphere of the earth together with the gravitational effects of the sun and moon give rise to a torque because the earth's axis of rotation is inclined at an angle (~23.5 deg) to the plane of the ecliptic. This torque causes the earth's axis of spin to rotate slowly anti-clockwise about a normal to the ecliptic. This rotation of the axis is referred to as precession. From this, it can be seen that the equinoxes will move slowly in a retrograde motion, along the ecliptic. The shift is about fifty seconds of arc per year. This means that although the first point of Aries was originally in the constellation Aries at the time of Hipparchus, it is now in the constellation Pisces and in about 24,000 years it will have come full circle, back to Aries. This is known as the precession of the equinoxes.

QUANTUM COSMOLOGY

In Quantum cosmology all events and positions in the universe are considered as a quantum (probability) wave function, labelled the 'wave function of the universe'. This means that the probability of many events and positions exist at the same time. This leads to the Many-Worlds Interpretation. See Chapter Five.

Quantum Superposition

The probability wave (see Quantum Wave Function) collapses when an experiment is conducted which relies upon the final position of the particles. Until this time, the wave shows the probability of the particles to be in different places at the same time. This is known as quantum superposition.

Quantum Theory (mechanics)

The physics of fundamental particles, e.g. protons, neutrons, electrons, etc, which can be considered both as waves and particles.

Quantum Tunnelling

A striking feature of quantum mechanics, whereby a particle can leak through a potential energy barrier that is classically opaque.

Quantum Wave Function

A fundamental particle can only be described as a probability wave, i.e. a wave related to the probability of finding the particle at a certain point in space if its energy is known.

Radioactive Dating

The half-life of a radioactive substance is the time taken for its radioactivity to be reduced by one half. Uranium 238 has a half-life of 4.5 billion years, Thorium 14 billion years, etc. The end product of the radioactive decay is helium and forms of lead. The ratios of helium and lead to the original radioactive substance in a structure gives the decay time, and hence the age of the structure.

Spectral Class Star

Stars are classified according to their absolute (intrinsic) magnitude and their chemical composition as evident from their spectra.

STRING THEORY

An attempt to combine gravity with quantum theory leads to certain mathematical inconsistencies called anomalies, which are replete with infinities. A theory, which replaces particles with strings as the fundamental objects of study, could possibly remove these anomalies, but a space of ten dimensions is required.

TABERNACLE

The portable shrine used by the ancient Israelites during their wanderings in the desert.

.

THRONE MYSTICISM

Early Jewish mysticism developed during the second and third centuries. It emphasised the gulf between God and Man. God was imagined as a great king who could only be approached through a perilous journey through the seven heavens. The journey focused upon the heavenly chariot seen by the prophet Ezekiel and embraced the idea of an imaginary process through the Divine dwelling to God's very throne.

WAVE FUNCTION OF THE UNIVERSE

See Quantum Cosmology.

Bibliography

ABELL, *Exploration of the Universe*, George O Abell, 1975, Holt, Rinehart and Winston, New York.

ALEXANDER, *The World's Religions*, Pat Alexander, (Organising Editor), 1982, Lion Publishing, Oxford.

ARMSTRONG, *A History of God*, Karen Armstrong, 1997, Mandarin Paperbacks, Random House, London.

ASHCROFT, *Life at the Extremes*, Francis Ashcroft, 2000, Harper Collins Publishers, London.

AXELROD, Robert Axelrod, *see Singer, Peter*, p88.

BELL, J S Bell, *Foundations of Physics*, 1983, 12, 989-99.

BERRY, *A Short History of Astronomy*, Arthur Berry, 1898 (republished 1961), Dover Publications Inc, USA

BORGES, *Labyrinths: Selected Stories and other Writings*, Jorge Luis Borges, Ed Donald A Yates and James E Irby, Penguin, London, UK, 1970, pp59ff.

BUTCHER and OEMLER, H Butcher, A Oemler, 1978, *Astrophysical Journal*, 226, 559.

BUTCHINS, 'Some Aspects of Extra Galactic Astrophysics', S A Butchins, DPhil Thesis, University of Oxford, 1983.

BYL, John Byl, the *Quarterly Journal of the Royal Astronomical Society*, Vol 37, No 3, September 1996, 369-371.

CAPRA, *The Tao of Physics*, Fritjof Capra, 1991, Harper Collins Publishers, London.

COLES and ELLIS, *Is the Universe Open or Closed?*, Peter Coles and George F R Ellis, 1997, Cambridge University Press, Cambridge

DAVIES, *Are We Alone?*, Paul Davies, 1995, Penguin Books, London

DAVIES, *God and the New Physics*, Paul Davies, 1983, Dent & Sons, London.

DAWKINS, *The Blind Watchmaker*, Richard Dawkins, 1986, Penguin Books, London.

DAWKINS, *Unweaving the Rainbow*, Richard Dawkins, 1998, Penguin Books, London.

DENNETT, *Consciousness Explained*, Daniel C Dennett, 1991, Penguin Books, London.

DENNETT, *Darwin's Dangerous Idea*, Daniel C Dennett, 1995, Penguin Press, London.

DE WAAL, Frans de Waal, *see* Singer, Peter, p97.

DIXON, *Man after Man*, Dougal Dixon, 1990, Blandford Press, London.

DREES, *Beyond the Big Bang*, Willem B Drees, 1990, Open Court Publishing Company, Illinois, USA.

DYSON, Freeman J Dyson, *Reviews of Modern Physics*, 1979, 51, 447-460.

DYSON, *Disturbing the Universe*, Freeman J Dyson, 1979, Harper and Row, 1981, Pan Books, London.

DYSON, *Infinite in all Directions*, Freeman J Dyson, 1988, Penguin Books, London.

ELLIS, *Before the Beginning*, Ellis, George F R, 1993, Bowerdean Publishing Co, London.

ELLIS and ALLEN, R S Ellis, D A Allen, 1983, *Monthly Notices of the Royal Astronomical Society*, 203, 685.

EVERETT, H Everett, *Rev Mod Physics*, 1957, 29, 454.

EVERY, *Christian Mythology*, George Every, 1970, Hamlyn, London.

FARHI and GUTH, E Farhi, & A H Guth, 1987, *Phys Lett* 183B, 149.

FERMI, Enrico Fermi referenced in Davies *Are We Alone*, p45.

FLOOD and DRESHER, Merril Flood & Melvin Dresher, *see* Ridley, p55.

FROHLICH, 'Long Range Coherence and energy storage in biological systems', H Frohlich, *Int Jour of Quantum Chem*, II, 1968, 641-649.

GELLATLY, ANGUS and ZATATE, *Mind and Brain for Beginners*, Gellatly, Angus and Zatate, Oscar, 1998, Icon Books, Cambridge.

GODWIN, *Angels an Endangered Species*, Malcolm Godwin, 1990, Boxtree, London.

GOULD, *An Urchin in the Storm*, Stephen Jay Gould, 1988, Penguin Books, London.

GOULD, *Ever Since Darwin*, Stephen Jay Gould, 1980, Penguin Books, London.

GREENFIELD, *The Human Brain*, Susan Greenfield, 1979, Weidenfeld & Nicolson, London.

GUTH, *The Inflationary Universe*, Alan H Guth, 1997, Jonathan Cape, London.

HARRISON, Edward R Harrison, *Quarterly Journal of the Royal Astronomical Society*, Vol 36, No 3, September 1995, 193-203.

HARRISON-BARBET, *Mastering Philosophy*, Anthony Harrison-Barbet, 1990, Macmillan Education, Basingstoke, UK.

HAWKING, *A Brief History of Time*, Stephen W Hawking, 1988, Transworld Publishers, London.

HAWKING and ELLIS, *The Large Scale Structure of Space-Time*, S W Hawking & G F R Ellis, 1973, Cambridge University Press, Cambridge.

HAWKING and PENROSE, *The Nature of Space and Time*, Stephen Hawking and Roger Penrose, 1996, Princeton University Press, Princeton, USA.

HETHERINGTON, *Cosmology: Historical, Literary, Philosophic, Religious and Scientific Perspectives*, edited by Norriss Hetherington, 1993, Garland Reference Library of Humanities, Volume 1634, Garland Publishing, London.

HOYLE, *The Intelligent Universe*, Fred Hoyle, 1983, Michael Joseph, London.

JACOBS, *We Have Reason to Believe*, Louis Jacobs, 1957, Vallentine Mitchell, London.

JOHNSON, *A History of the Jews*, Paul Johnson, 1987, Weidenfield and Nicolson, London.

JOHNSON, *A History of Christianity*, Paul Johnson, 1976, Weidenfield and Nicolson, London.

JORDAN [http://www.near-death.com/experiences/experts6.html], Dr Robert Jordan, E-MAIL rjordan@prysm.net

KAUFFMAN, *At Home in the Universe*, Stuart A Kauffman, 1995, Penguin Books, London.

KAUFFMAN, *The Origins of Order*, Stuart A Kauffman, 1993, Oxford University Press, Oxford.

KRON, R G Kron, 1980, *Astrophysical Journal Supplement*, Supp, 43, 1

LEAKEY, *The Sixth Extinction*, Richard Leakey, 1995, Phoenix, London.

LEWIS, *Christian Reflections*, C S Lewis, Fount Paperbacks, Collins, Glasgow.

LEWIS, *God in the Dock*, C S Lewis, Fount Paperbacks, Collins, Glasgow.

LINDE, Andrei Linde, *Scientific American*, Spring 1998, Volume 9, Number 1, p98.

MALINSKI, Manfred Malinski, *see* Ridley, p79.

MURPHY and ELLIS, *On the Moral Nature of the Universe*, Nancy Murphy, and George F R Ellis, R, 1996, Fortress Press, Minneapolis.

NASR, *An Introduction to Islamic Cosmological Doctrine*, S H Nasr, 1964, 1978, Harvard University Press, Cambridge, USA.

O'CONNER, *Free Will*, D J O'Conner, Ancor Books Edition 1971, Doubleday, Garden City, New York.

PEACOCK, *A Brief History of Eternity*, Roy E Peacock, 1989, Monarch Publications, Eastbourne, UK.

PEAT, *Superstrings*, F David Peat, 1991, Abacus, London.

PEEBLES et al, 'The Evolution of the Universe', James P Peebles, E Schramm, David N Turner, Edward L Kron, *Scientific American*, October 1994.

PENROSE, *Shadows of the Mind*, Roger Penrose, 1994, Oxford University Press, Oxford.

PENROSE, *The Emperor's New Mind*, Roger Penrose, 1990, Vintage, London.

PENROSE, *The Large, the Small and the Human Mind*, Roger Penrose, 1997, Cambridge University Press, Cambridge.

PFEIFFER, *The Emergence of Man*, John E Pfeiffer, 1973, Cardinal Edition, Sphere Books, London.

POLKINGHORNE, *Beyond Science*, John Polkinghorne, 1996, The Press Syndicate of the University of Cambridge, Cambridge.

POLKINGHORNE, *Science and Christian Belief*, John Polkinghorne, 1994, The Society for Promoting Christian Knowledge, London.

RAMACHANDRAN and BLAKESLEE, *Phantoms in the Brain*, V S Ramachandran, & Sandra Blakeslee, 1998, Fourth Estate, London.

RAPAPORT, Anatol Rapaport, *see* Ridley p60.

REES, *Before the Beginning*, Martin Rees, 1997, Simon and Schuster, London.

RIDLEY, *The Origins of Virtue*, Matt Ridley, 1997, Penguin Books, London.

ROSE, *From Brains to Consciousness*, Steven Rose, Editor, 1998, Penguin Books, London..

ROSE, *The Conscious Brain*, Steven Rose, 1973, Penguin Books, London.

ROTHMAN and ELLIS, T Rothman, and G F R Ellis, *Quarterly Journal of the Royal Astronomical Society*, Vol 34, No 2, June 1993, 201-212.

RUSSELL, *History of Western Philosophy*, Bertrand Russell, 1971, George Allen & Unwin, London.

RUSSELL, *The Basic Writings of Bertrand Russell*, Bertrand Russell, 1961, Simon and Schuster, New York.

RUSSELL, *Wisdom of the West*, Bertrand Russell, 1959, Macdonald, London.

SABOM, *Recollections of Death*, Michael B Sabom, 1982, Harper and Row, New York.

SCHROEDER, *Genesis and the Big Bang*, Gerald L Schroeder, 1990, Bantam Books, New York.

SEARLE, *The Mystery of Consciousness*, John R Searle, 1997, Granta Publications, London.

SHANKS et al, Shanks et al, 1983, *Monthly Notices of the Royal Astronomical Society*, 202, 1245.

SHKLOVSKII, *Intelligent Life in the Universe*, I S Shklovskii, Carl Sagan, 1966, Dell Publishing, USA.

SILK, *The Big Bang*, Joseph Silk, 1980, W H Freeman and Co, Oxford.

SINGER, 'The Cosmology of Giordana Bruno (1548-1600)', Dorothea Walley Singer, *Isis* Vol XXXIII, Pt 2, No 88, June 1941, 187-196

SINGER, *Ethics*, Edited by Peter Singer, 1994, Oxford University Press, Oxford.

SMOLIN, L Smolin, *Classical and Quantum Gravity*, 1992, Vol 9 173-191.

SMOLIN, *The Life of the Cosmos*, L Smolin, 1997, Weidenfield and Nicolson, London.

SMOOT, *Wrinkles in Time*, George Smoot, 1993, Little Brown and Co (UK), London.

SNEATH, *Planets and Life*, P H A Sneath, 1970, Minerva Press, New York.

SPENCE, *Introduction to Mythology*, Lewis Spence, 1921, George G Harrap & Company, 1994, London.

STANNARD, *The God Experiment*, Russell Stannard, 1999, Faber and Faber, London.

STEEL, Duncan Steel, *The Observatory*, 1995 April, Vol 115, 78-83.

TARNAS, *The Passion of the Western Mind*, Richard Tarnas, 1991, Ballantine Books, Random House, New York.

TAYLER, *The Stars: Their Structure and Evolution*, R J Tayler, 1981, Wykeham Publications, London.

TEILHARD de CHARDIN, *The Phenomenon of Man*, Teilhard de Chardin, Pierre, 1975, Harper and Row, New York.

TIPPLER, *The Physics of Immortality*, J Frank Tippler, 1994, Macmillan, London.

WEINBERG, *Gravitation and Cosmology*, Steven Weinberg, 1971, John Wiley and Sons, New York, London, Sydney, Toronto.

WEINBERG, *The First Three Minutes*, Steven Weinberg, 1977, Andre Deutsch, London.

WHITE, *A History of the Warfare of Science with Theology in Christendom*, Vols 1 and 2, A D White, 1896 (republished 1960), Dover Publications, USA.

WHITE, *Isaac Newton The Last Sorcerer*, Michael White, 1997, Fourth Estate, London.

WILKINSON, *Alone in the Universe*, David Wilkinson, 1997, Monarch Publications, Crowborough, East Sussex.

WOOLDRIDGE, *Mechanical Man*, Dean E Wooldridge, 1968, McGraw-Hill Book Company, New York.

WRIGHT, Wright, S, 'The Roles of Mutation, Inbreeding, Crossbreeding and Selection in Evolution', *Proceedings of the Sixth International Congress on Genetics*, 1:356, 1932.

Index

A

A Brief History of Eternity 8
A Brief History of Time 8, 91
A Free Mans' Worship 119
Abell, George, O 77
Abraham 3, 62, 67, 192, 195
Absolute pantheism 142
Adam 62, 111, 112, 139, 192
age of the universe 67, 70, 71,
        81, 86, 102, 112
Ahura Mazda 146
al-Battani 237, 239
al-Biruni 29, 67
al-Shatir 237, 239
al-Tusi 237, 239
Alcmaeon of Croton 153
Allah 28, 54, 196, 224
Almagest 8
Alone in the Universe 8, 57
Alpha Centauri 47
Anabaptist tradition 209
Anabaptist/Quaker 208
Anaximander 21
Anaximenes 21
Andromeda spiral galaxy 60
Angra Mainyu 146, 148
Anselm 132
Anthropic Principle
        109, 113, 120, 136
Antiochus Epiphanes 37
Apollonius 99

aquamorph 79, 80
archetypal forms 16, 24, 28
Are We Alone? 151
Aristarchus 24, 29, 31, 33, 42
Aristotle **25**, 26, 27, 33,
        41, 99, 142, 149, 199
artificial intelligence 159, 160, 161
astrology 29
At Home in the Universe 58
atheism 37, 40, 57, 135
atheist 6, 10, 82, 193
Axelrod, Robert 201
Ayer, A J 54, 203, 204
Aztec 18

B

Babylon 18, 19
Babylonian epic 20
bacteria 59, 139
Beatrice 3
Before the Beginning 105, 210
Bell, J S 72, 97
Bemidbar 192
Bergson 165
Big Bang, actions of God 131
Big Bang, COBE as confirmation 107
Big Bang, confirmation 72
Big Bang, described in Taoism 189
Big Bang, from Olbers paradox 74
Big Bang, history of the universe 86
Big Bang, in black holes 114
Big Bang, inflationary universe 101

Big Bang, initial conditions of the universe 88
Big Bang, measurement of time 71
Big Bang, origin of the universe 73
Big Bang, parallel universe 167
Big Bang, production of hydrogen and helium 72
Big Bang, standard model 110
Big Bang, the Vatican 78
Big Bang, tunnelling process 166
black holes, and stars 118
black holes, by natural selection 117
black holes, event horizon 91
black holes, formation of universes 114
black holes, intelligent life 121
black holes, maximum production of 115
black holes, not amenable to observation 119
black holes, novae and supernovae 87
black holes, origin of universes 136
black holes, other universes 166
black holes, parameters of physics 116
black holes, scenarios for galaxy formation 88
Blakeslee, S 152
Blind Watchmaker, The 82, 94, 116
Boethius 132
Borde, Arvind 105
Borges, Jorge Luis 97
Bounteous Immortals 146
Brahe, Tycho 34
Brahma 19, 140
Brahmin 140, 141
Bruno, Giordano 1, 2, 31, 32
Buddha 41, 185, 186, 187
Buddhism 41, 185, 186, 188, 190, 207
Buridan 33
Butcher and Oemler 74
Byl, John 122

C

Calvin, John 36, 67
Capra, Fritjof 191
carbon 90
Carnot, Sadi 76
Carter, Brandon 109, 136
Cartesian Theatre 158
Cassini, Giovanni Dominic 43
Cayenne 43
celestial spheres 27, 34
Chaldea 19
Chalmers, Thomas 56, 62, 152
Charvakas 40
Chinese 18, 97, 188
chosen race 194
Christ 62, 67, 148, 194, 195, 198, 213, 217
Christian Research Institute 178
Christianity 194
  Jesus Christ the one and only saviour 222
Christianity and Judaism, dualism 147
Christianity, and Marxism 40
Christianity, Copernican Principle 198
Christianity, exclusivity 194
Christianity, fundamental beliefs 194
Christianity, geocentric doctrine 31
Christianity, in other worlds 56
Christianity, marginalisation 199
Christianity, Platonic forms 27
Chuang-tzu 189
Cleanthes 24
Clerk-Maxwell 9
COBE 107, 108
Cohen 139
Coles, Peter 77, 106, 125
comet 77
Communism 5, 40
conditions
  for life on a planet 232
Confucian Analects 188
Confucianism 188, 189, 190

Conscious Brain, The 17
Consciousness 129, 151, 159
Consciousness Explained 129
conversion 173, 197, 198
Copernican Principle 6
Copernican Principle, and Buddhism 41
Copernican Principle, and conflict 205
Copernican Principle, and ethical foundations of religion igion 205
Copernican Principle, Anthropic Principle 109
Copernican Principle, C S Lewis 56
Copernican Principle, confirmation of 35
Copernican Principle, demotion of Man 194
Copernican Principle, denial required 63
Copernican Principle, extra galactic civilisations 50
Copernican Principle, Galileo 34
Copernican Principle, Giordano Bruno 2
Copernican Principle, invalidation of fundamentalism 151, 198
Copernican Principle, invocation by Einstein 10
Copernican Principle, no Muslim opposition 199
Copernican Principle, Parsis 185
Copernican Principle, post-Copernican world 17
Copernican Principle, recognition 9
Copernican Principle, reincarnation 207
Copernican Principle, rejection of 8, 12
Copernican Principle, statement of 7
Copernican Principle Theistic argument lost 206
Copernican Revolution, The 34

Copernicus **xx**, 2, 10, 32, 33, 35, 36, 42, 114, 216
cosmogony 18
Cosmological Principle 9, 10, 42
Cosmos Indicapleustes 30
creation ex nihilo 29, 30

D

Dahriyun 28
Dante, Alighieri 3, **4**, 56
Darwin, Charles 12, 82, 83, **84**, 112, 116, 136
Davies, Paul 151, 216
Dawkins, Richard 10, 15, 17, 64, 82, 83, 85, 94, 109, 119
de Cheseaux, J L 73
de Cusa, Nicholas 2, 31, 42
De Revolutionibus Orbium Celestium 32
de Waal, Frans 202
degrees Kelvin 71, 72, 111
Deicide
Jews deemed guilty 223
Deism 7, 63, 136, 137, 142, 206
Democritus 21, 177, 182
demons 145, 146, 148, 160
Dennett 12, 15, 19, 129, 152, 58, 159, 160, 161, 164, 182
Descartes, René 21, 156, **157**
Deuteronomy 193
Devil 148, 149
dialectic materialism 189
Dicke, Robert 71
Digges, Thomas 32, 34
dimension 12, 13
Disturbing the Universe 85
Divine Comedy, The 3
Dixon, Dougal 79, 81
DNA 54, 90
Drake, Frank 47, 65
Drees, Willem 13, 124, 129, 130, 131, 132, 133, 134, 135, 137
Dresher, Melvin 201

dualism 145, 147, 148, 158, 161, 165, 182, 207
Dyson, Freeman 80, 85, 127, 128, 131, 137, 143, 149

E

Earth Goddess 18
Einstein, Albert 9, 10, **11,** 13, 35, 42, 86, 91, 101, 103, 111, 114
Ellis, George F R 77, 91, 106, 117, 118, 125, 136
Ellis, R S 74
Emperors 'New Mind, The 92, 129
Enuma Elish 19
Epicures 21
Erasistratus 153
eschatology
  prophetic vision 223
Eternal Inflation and the Initial Singularity 105
ethics 7, 100, 200
Euclid 21
Eve 140, 192, 211
Everett, H 96, 99, 107, 126, 143, 150, 166, 206
evolution,
  of the spirit 229
evolution, Anaximander and Anaximenes 21
evolution, and increasing complexity 122
evolution, and natural selection 70
evolution, and religious experience 175
evolution, and the Omega point 124
evolution, and the transmigration of souls 41
evolution, application of biological to cosmological 59, 60, 117
evolution, Assyrian inscriptions 19
evolution, by divine favour 58
evolution, chance mutations 8
evolution, conflict inevitable 205
evolution, cosmology 12

evolution, future projections 81
evolution, galactic models 71
evolution, generalised to the cosmos 136
evolution, invalidates Paleys argument 94
evolution, natural selection 112
evolution, not necessarily progressive 167
evolution, of co-operation 202
evolution, of intelligence on planets 169
evolution, of man 87
evolution, of reciprocity 203
evolution, of sentience 200
evolution, of the universe 74
evolution, of universes 114
evolution, on earth 79
evolution, on life bearing planets 49
evolution, scientific thought 31
evolution, self organisation 112
evolution, source of conflict 165
evolution the normal distribution 169
evolution, the weak Anthropic Principle 109
evolution, time 120
Exodus 192
Exploration of the Universe 77
extra-terrestrial civilisations 47

F

Falsafah 28
false vacuum 103, 104, 105
Faraday 9
Faustus Siconus 143
Fermi, Enrico 59, 60, 65
First Three Minutes, The 86
fitness landscape 9
fitness value 9
Fitzgerald, Edward 211
Flood, Merrill 201
Four Noble Truths 186
Fraunhofer, Joseph 35

Free Will 64
free will 64

G

Gabriel 196
Galen 153
Galileo 9, 26, 32,
    33, 34, 36, 42, 43, 78
Garden of Forking Paths, The 97
Gautama, Siddarther 185
Gell-Mann, Murray 166
General Theory of Relativity 10, 91
Genesis, and Enuma Elish 19
Genesis and the Big Bang 17
Genesis, Christian cosmology 30
Genesis, comparison with the Big Bang 110
Genesis, earth not stated as the only planet 194
Genesis, esoteric 215
Genesis, first book of the Torah 192
Genesis, literal truth 136
Genesis, Maimonides 113
Genesis, natural development of life 112
Genesis, proper time 112
Genesis, symbolic 29
Genesis, The biblical God 20
Genesis, the wrong order of creation 39
Genesis, transparent universe 111
Genesis, two accounts of creation 66
Geroch, R P 91
God Experiment, The 218, 220, 222
God in the Dock 8
Godel 161
Golden Age 29
Gospels 195
Gosse, Edmund 63, 64
Gould, Stephen Jay 109, 167
Gravitation and Cosmology 70
Greek enlightenment 21, 24
Greeks 21, 22, 37, 55, 75, 153

Greenfield, Susan 128
greenhouse effect 77
Guth 100, 102, 103, 104,
    106, 108, 121, 127
Guth, Alan 6

H

Hadith 238, 240
Hainaut, Oliver 61, 65
Hameroff, S R 152
Hamin al-Ghazzali, Abu 28
Harrison, Edward R
    121, 122, 136, 166, 206
Hassan, Usama 235
Hawking 6, 8, 64, 91,
    92, 93, 94, 121, 129, 166
heat death 75, 77, 81, 105, 119, 129
heaven 2, 3, 57, 67, 99, 188, 200
helium 35, 45, 53,
    71, 72, 73, 86, 89, 90, 111
hell 2, 3, 57, 99, 200
Herophilus 153
Herschel, William 47, 50, 51
Hindu 19, 41, 185
Hinyana 187
Hippocrates 153
Hobbes, Thomas 200
Homo sapiens 17
Horkheimer, Max 100
Hoyle, Fred 58, 59, 65, 73, 90, 122
Hubble, Edwin 51, 52, 65, 213
Human Brain, The 128
hydrogen 45, 52, 53, 71,
    72, 73, 86, 89, 90, 111

I

Ikhwan 28
incarnation 63, 194
Incas 19
India 22, 29, 122,
    139, 145, 147, 185, 191
infanticide 198
Inflationary Universe, The 101, 103

intelligent life 7, 8, 48, 56, 61, 93, 121, 169, 194, 228
Internet 152, 178, 181
Iragui, Vincent 174
Is the Universe Open or Closed? 77, 106
Islam 28, 30, 194, 195, 198, 199
Islam, Copernican Principle 198
Islam, Platonic forms 27

J

Jacobs, Louis 57, 65, 131, 226
Jainism 139, 184, 207
Japan 187, 190
Jehovah 20, 21, 55, 144
Jekyll, Dr and Mr Hyde 158
Jesus 75, 147, 194, 195, 213, 217
Jesus Christ, C S Lewis 55
Jordan, Robert 178, 182
Judaism 192
Judaism, a young religion 70
Judaism and Christianity
    man reduced 53
Judaism Christianity and Islam
    pre-Copernican 41
    superstition 143
    Western Religions 7
Judaism, Copernican Principle 198
Judaism, distinction between human and divine 37
Judaism, ethical principles 228
Judaism, Kabbalah 149
Judaism, Liberal Judaism 227
Judaism, mankind the central issue 192
Judaism, progressive view of the Torah 193
Judaism, secularisation 199
Judaism, unique contribution 228
Judgement Day 71, 75, 81, 198
Justinian 28

K

Kabbalah 143, 149, 199
Kant, Immanual 50

Kathir 238
Kauffman, Stuart 9, 65
Kenosis 208
Kepler, Johannes 34, 43
kindling 173, 174
Kirchhoff, Gustav 35
Kitt Peak 60, 61
Koch 139
Koran, creation greater than mankind 53
Koran, expansion of space 39
Koran, intervention of God in history 199
Koran, legal rights for women 198
Koran, literal truth 79
Koran, Muhammad 196
Koran, no forcible conversion 198
Koran, purpose of stars 54
Koran, reading as a spiritual experience 198
Koran, recited aloud 196
Koran, special pleading 39
Koran, spiritual world 28
Koran, the revelation 196
Koran, the use of reason 197
Koran, tolerance of Jews and Christians 197
Koran, transcendental interpretation 199
Koran, wealth to be shared 197

L

Lao-tzu 189
Large Scale Structure of Space-Time, The 91
Large, the Small and the Human Mind, The 106
Leeuwenhoek, Anton van 139
legions of demons 148, 149
Leibniz 210
Leviticus 192
Lewis, C S 8, 54, 55, 56, 57, 65, 152, 194

Libet, B 152
Life of the Cosmos 116, 118, 136
Lightfoot, John 67
Linde, Andrei 105, 108
Lings, Martin 237
Lord Kelvin 9
Lost Horizon, The 152
Lucifer 3
Lucretius 22
Luther, Martin 36, 148

M

Maccabees 37
Madam Blavatsky 185
Mahayana 187, 188
Man after Man 79, 80, 81
Many Worlds Theory 65, 96
Mars 34, 43, 45, 48, 59, 77, 152
Martianus Capella 31
meditation 151, 183, 185, 189,
 190, 191
microwave background
 71, 73, 87, 93, 107, 122
Middle Ages 149, 153
Milinsky, Manfred 202
Milky Way 34, 47, 50, 53, 72
Milton, James 152
Mishna 193
Modified pantheism 142
Moral Nature of the Universe, The 208
Moses 110, 112, 143, 192, 193
Moses Maimonides 112
Moses of Leon 143
Mount Olympus 55
Mount Wilson 48, 51
Muhammad 54, 195, 196, 197, 198
Muruwah 195
Muslim religion 197
mutation 9, 169, 175

N

Nahmanides 110
natural selection, and conflict 165
natural selection, and Darwin 116
natural selection, and genetic engineering 79
natural selection, and intelligence 49
natural selection, and near-man 8
natural selection, and Newtonian time
 120
natural selection, and the brain 171
natural selection, evolutionary model
 118
natural selection, free will 203
natural selection, invalidates God 12
natural selection, man made universes
 121
natural selection, moral values 134
natural selection, of universes
 114, 136
natural selection, purposeful life-forms
 85
natural selection, Schroeders argument
 112
Natural Theology 82, 223
Nazism 5, 216
NDE, Near-death Experience
 176, 177, 178, 181
Neanderthals 113
Near-death Experience 176
neurologists 5
New Testament 75, 148
Newton, Sir Isaac 9, 34, 43, 67, 97,
 100, 120, 140
Nirvana 186, 187, 188, 200
noble eightfold Path 186
Nominalist 27, 33
non-violence 208, 209
normal distribution 112, 167, 169
Numbers 192
numinous 18, 55

O

Ockhams' Razor 27
   Multi-universe contravenes 221
OConnor, D J 64
Olbers Paradox 73
Old Testament 30, 173, 192
Omega Point 124, 125, 126, 131
Omphalos 63
On The Heavens 26
Oresme 33
Origins of Order, The 49, 58
Origins of Virtue, The 204
Osiris 19

P

Pachacamac 19
pagan 2, 5, 198
Paine, Thomas 37, **38**, 39
Paley, William 82, 83, 85, 88, 94,
   95, 98, 104, 109, 206
Pali Cannon 187
Pandora Problem 138
panspermia 59
pansychic 160
pantheism 40, 133, 143, 149
Paradise 3, 145
parallax 43
parallel universe, and consciousness
   150
parallel universe, brains temporal lobes
   182
parallel universe, conflict 205
parallel universe, cosmologically
   respectable 206
parallel universe, ethics 203
parallel universe, evidence 166
parallel universe, laws of physics 151
parallel universe, Near-death Experience 175
parallel universe, Nirvana 187
parallel universe, not a Deistic
   argument 200

parallel universe, paranormal 167
parallel universe, religious ideas 199
parallel universe, source of conflict
   164
parallel universe, supernatural
   152, 182
parallel universe, universal dualism
   165
paranormal 166, 167, 169, 182
Parsis 147, 185
Pascal 9
Passion of the Western Mind, The 16
Pasteur 139
Peacock 8
Penzias, Arno and Wilson, Robert 72
Persinger, Michael 171
Peter Martyr 67
Phantoms in the Brain 171
Philo 30
Philolaus 22
Physics 26
Physics of Immortality, The 75, 124
Picard, Jean 43
Plato 24, **25**, 26, 27, 28, 41, 108,
   123, 140, 167, 205
Plato's Theory of Forms 26
Polkinghorne, Rev Dr John
   135, 212, 219, 220, 221, 222, 223
Pope Pius XII 79
Principia 34
Prisoners' Dilemma, The 201
Progressive Judaism 147
prokaryotic cells 70
proper time 66, 86, 112
Proxima Centauri 47
psychokinesis 200
Ptolemaic theory 31
Ptolemy 8, 29, 114
Pythagoras 21

Q

Qatadah, Abu 54
quantum cosmology 18, 92, 95

Quantum Theory and the Brain 152
quantum wave function 132, 150
quasars 3
Quraysh 196, 197
Qureshi, Shoaib 241

R

radioactive dating 64
Ramachandran, V S
   152, 158, 159, 171, 173, 174, 182
Ramadan 195
Rapoport, Anatol 202
Realist school 27
Recollections of Death 176
redshift 51
Rees, Martin 105, 108
Reformation 36
Renaissance 3
Richer, Jean 43
Ridley, Matt 204
Rolston, Holmes 209
Roman Catholic Church 33, 36
Roman Empire 27
Rome 18
Rose, Steven 17, 152
Rothman, T 117, 118, 136
Russell, Bertrand 119
Russian Doll Multiverse 117

S

Sabom, Professor Michael
   175, 176, 178, 182
Satanists 145
Schelling, Friedrich von 143, 149
Schmidt, Martin 48
Schroeder, Gerald 17, 110, 111,
   112, 113, 136, 216
Science and Christian
   219, 220, 222, 224
Science of God, The 17, 110, 112
Scotti, Jim 60, 61, 65
Searle, John 159
second coming 62, 75, 105, 194, 195

Shadows of the Mind
   129, 152, 164, 170
Shakespeare, William 56, 140, 211
Shinto 190
Shroff, Behramshah 185
Shumaker 77
Sikh 183, 184
singularity, and inflation theory 105
singularity, and the Omega point 125
singularity, and tunnelling 114
singularity, avoidance of 93
singularity, beginning of the universe
   92
singularity, definition 91
singularity, evidence for 117
singularity, Hawkings solution 93
singularity, manufacture of universes
   121
singularity, measurement of time 86
singularity, Penroses acceptance of 94
singularity, rebounds 115
singularity, serial universes 98
singularity, universe within a 117
Sistine Chapel 203
skyhooks 16, 160
Smolin, Lee 6, 12, 114, 115, 116,
   117, 118, 119, 120, 121, 136, 166
Smoot, George 107
soul, and Deism 142
soul, differentiates man from beasts
   113
soul, drawn towards the purity of
   being 142
soul, evolution of 70
soul, in the pineal gland 158
soul, manifest in man 214
soul, site of 153
soul, survival of bodily death 170
soul, universal compared to the human
   29
space telescope 52, 65, 213
Special Theory of Relativity 9, 101
spectroscope 10

spectroscopy 35, 52, 56, 71
sphericity of the earth 22
Spinoza 148
spirituality
    integrated with free will 222
St Athanasius 66
St Augustine 27, 62
St Clement of Alexandria 31
St Isadore 31
St Paul 62
St Philastrius 30
Stannard, Rev Dr Russell 212, 218,
    220, 221, 222, 223
Steady State 73, 74, 103, 108
Steel, Duncan 60
Stevenson, Louis 158
string theory 13
sub-cortical parts of the brain 153
Sufi 28
Sufis 28, 199
supernatural 123, 145, 152,
    166, 173, 182, 200
supernovae 87
superposition 96, 126, 134, 150, 166
Surat al-Talaq 238

T

Tabari 238
Tabernacle 192
Tafsir al-Jalalayn 236
Talmud 193
Tao 189, 191
Taoism 188, 189
Tarnas, Richard 16
Tecoma, Evelyn 174
Teilhard de Chardin, Pierre 124
telepathy 169, 182, 200
Thabit ibn Qurra 239
Thales 21
The God Experiment 229
Theism 142, 143, 206
Theory of Emotions, William James
    and Carl Lange 179

Theosophical Society 185
Thermodynamics 75, 76, 186
Thrasymachus 205
time dilation 9, 111
Tippler, Frank 75, 80, 124,
    125, 126, 127, 128, 131, 137
TIT FOR TAT 202
Tlalocs 19
Torah, Abraham 195
Torah, and modern cosmology 110
Torah, and Satan 148
Torah, as the Old Testament 30
Torah, cannot be changed 224
Torah, dictated by God to Moses 192
Torah, divine intervention 112
Torah, free interpretation of 110
Torah, Leviticus 192
Torah, literal truth 79
Torah, narratives of creation 19
Torah, not meant to be scientific 193
Torah, Numbers 192
Torah, pleasing the rabbis 113
Torah, problem of the pre-eminence of
    Humanity 57
Torah, true to the imagination of the
    human mind 113
Torah, word of God 193
Tsui Pen 97
Tucker, A W 201
tunnelling concept 114

U

UFO 58, 60, 78
uncertainty principle 91
Universal Soul 28, 29
universals 26
Unweaving the Rainbow 17

V

vacumorph 80
Valhalla 151
Vatican 78
Vedas 40, 203

Vilenkin, Alexander 105
Vishnu Purana 19
Vishtasp 146
Voltaire 140, 141
Von Neumann machines 60

W

Waraqa ibn Nawfal 196
We Have Reason to Believe 57, 131
Weinberg, Steven 70, 86, 166
West, Richard 61, 65
West, the 37
Whewell, William 56
Wickramasinghe, Chandra 58, 59, 65
Wilkinson, Rev David
        8, 57, 58, 59, 62
William of Ockham 27, 33
Witten, Edward 13
Wittgenstein 54
Wooldridge, Dean E 64
Wright, S 8
Wright, Thomas 47

Z

Zeus 33, 37, 138
Zohar 143
Zoroaster 146, 147
Zoroastrianism 145, 147, 148, 149